CURIOUS C
OLD YORKSHIRE

A collection of remedies, health superstitions and medical memories

Dulcie Lewis

COUNTRYSIDE BOOKS
NEWBURY · BERKSHIRE

COUNTRYSIDE BOOKS
3 Catherine Road
Newbury, Berkshire

To view our complete range of books,
please visit us at
www.countrysidebooks.co.uk

ISBN 1 85306 694 X

Front cover photo by
Ann Holubecki and Josephine Hopper

Designed by Graham Whiteman

Produced through MRM Associates Ltd., Reading
Typeset by Techniset Typesetters, Newton-le-Willows
Printed by Woolnough Bookbinding Ltd., Irthlingborough

CONTENTS

Foreword   7

10 Pieces of Advice   8

Medical Matters   9

Short, Sharp and Not Particularly Sweet   15

Getting It Off Your Chest   21

The Glorious Goose   28

Whooping Cough   30

Those Were the Days   34

Cold Comfort   35

Owler Star's Healing Waters   39

Headache   42

Earache   44

Toothache   46

A Day in the Life   49

The Internal Workings   50

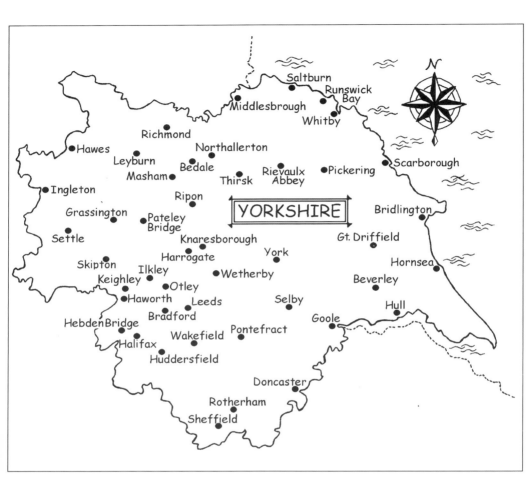

This book is about the remedies and health superstitions of old Yorkshire and my research has extended to the 'true' Yorkshire county boundaries before the changes of 1974. In the text, an asterisk denotes a remedy not from Yorkshire but too interesting to leave out!

The Rites of Spring   57

A Rash of Boils and Other Eruptions   60

Warts   69

Kidding Pills   72

Pain in the Neck   74

The Cures   77

Pains, Sprains and Chilblains   79

Pre Penicillin   89

Leeches   93

Women's Business   97

Keeping Up Your Strength   104

Stinking 'Spaws'   108

10 Top Tips from Yorkshire   112

ACKNOWLEDGEMENTS

I have received so much generous help with the writing of this book: from people who took the time to write and phone, those who gave me access to much loved family 'commonplace' books, pharmacists and the retired doctor I badgered for enlightenment and clarification.

A very special mention must be made to my friend Ann Holubecki for all her assistance, especially with the photographs.

Also Mac Webster of Dinnington, Sheffield, who shared with me his enthusiasm and knowledge about this subject but who sadly died before the book was completed.

Special thanks too must go to those northern newspapers who were kind enough to help me with my search for old remedies:

The Northern Echo
Darlington and Stockton Times
Craven Herald
The Star Sheffield
Telegraph and Argus
Whitby Gazette
Rotherham Star
Brighouse Echo
Leeds Express.

Two museums have been particularly helpful and for those interested in this subject they are well worth visiting:

The Thackray Medical Museum, Leeds, especially the librarian Alan Humphries.
The Dales Countryside Museum at Hawes.

★ ★ ★ ★ ★

This book is dedicated to my husband Ray for doing all the washing up while I was writing it.

FOREWORD

I have no medical experience whatsoever: my healing and nursing skills are zero. A quick shuffle through the Lewis medicine cabinet, an untidy drawer in the kitchen, will reveal: some odd size elastoplasts, a bottle of paracetomol, a half-eaten box of Rennies and some antihistamine ointment for the Yorkshire midges. This family has never possessed a thermometer!

I was born in 1945, the National Health Service in 1948. Like many people who have never known a time when free medicine was not available to all, I expect a doctor to put me right. If I am ill a quick blast of some pills with minimum inconvenience to my busy life and I should be on my feet again. I have come to expect too much of our medical services.

My interest in medical remedies came only while writing my last book. *Down the Yorkshire Pan* was a humorous look at how the people of North Yorkshire kept themselves clean, decent and healthy in the past. The privy down the garden or out in the yard featured prominently. In conversations, once you stirred up memories of childhood adventures in a privy, the topic of constipation always followed: the weekly purge was part of childhood. I was offered many recommendations on how to keep regular together with other cures used by Mother. In the book I included a chapter on cures for the three Cs – coughs, colds and constipation, but on completion I found I had a wealth of wisdom that could not be included.

Some of the cures will make no sense to us now, others are downright dangerous, but others have an element of commonsense. As a retired farmer's wife remarked, 'We often took the right thing but didn't know why it worked.'

Certain ingredients can no longer be obtained. Neither camphorated tincture of opium, known as Paregoric, used in many home-made cough medicines, or the all pervasive camphorated oil are to be bought over the counter from the local pharmacist or herbalist. Which is perhaps just as well.

It hardly seems necessary to point out that if you were to try the more simple remedies recorded in this book you do so entirely at your own risk. I do not recommend, neither have I tested, any of them and whilst a spoonful of blackcurrant jelly added to hot water might be soothing for a sore throat, roasted mouse for whooping cough is not a good idea.

Dulcie Lewis

10 PIECES OF ADVICE

*'In uncommon or complicated diseases or where life is more
immediately in danger, apply to a Physician that fears God.'
John Wesley's Primitive Physic.*

- More people are slain by late suppers than by the sword.

- The best Physicians are Drs Diet-quiet and Merryman.

- The best physic is fresh air; the best pill, plain fare.

- Too many pills injure health, and too much doctor's physic often brings patients down to a shadow.

- To become hardy, gradually accustom yourself to less clothing.

- Whilst in a sick-room smoke a cigarette in cases of fever, and do not swallow your spittle.

- First the Distiller, then the Doctor, then the Undertaker.

- Delicate persons should take light suppers.

- All pickled, smoked or salted and high-seasoned food is unholesome (sic).

- The healthiest feast costs the least.

★ ★ ★ ★ ★

The above advice is taken from *600 Valuable Home Recipes – Save Doctors'
Fees* published in Middlesbrough sometime in the last century. It was
found by Mary Nolan of Stockton on Tees when clearing out the home
of her mother-in-law Katy Nolan after her death at the age of 93. Katy
Nolan lived in Thornaby on Tees and was typical of the many unsung
heroines of Yorkshire family life. A great cook whose house and washing
were immaculate and who could tackle anything when it came to
practical matters and the care of her family.

MEDICAL MATTERS

'England is the place for pills and Englishmen are the dupes that swallow them.' Frederick Smith Garlick, a Halifax Doctor 1847.

There has never been a shortage of people claiming they could do you some good: mostly they ministered to you at your peril. The earliest exception was the Church. The great monastic houses of Yorkshire lived a healthy regular life with clean running water, organised systems of sewage disposal and some knowledge of the healing properties of plants. Rievaulx Abbey had an unusually large infirmary and caring for the sick was part of the Cistercian ministry. However, any medical knowledge gained in the monastic infirmaries was lost with the Dissolution of the Monasteries by Henry VIII in 1536.

In 1997 Rod Hall was given permission by the Congregational Church in Reeth, Swaledale to cultivate a patch of land behind the church and here he created a medieval 'physik garden'. Bergamot, rue, lovage, clary sage, sweet cicely, comfrey and myrtle are among the many medieval plants growing in this lovely spot. (Rod Hall)

Henry made some amends towards the sick by granting a royal charter to the Barber-Surgeons Company in 1540. A red and white striped pole advertised their expertise in cutting and chopping; the red representing the colour of blood.

The pecking order in the medical world then was physicians, barber-surgeons and, lowest of all, apothecaries. All would attempt, for a price, some healing. The physician in England was educated, mostly at Oxford or Cambridge Universities, but the barber-surgeons were craftsmen whose crude medical skills were passed from father to son after a long apprenticeship. If you could not face either of these professions, the apothecary would try to cure you with his knowledge of plants.

For centuries, healing by medical men consisted of either starving the patient, bleeding, purging, or cupping. For this last a tightly fitting vessel filled with steam was applied to part of the body and the vessel allowed to cool. Any operations performed by surgeons up to the end of the 19th century were restricted mainly to amputations or cutting for a stone in the bladder – nothing that went too deep. The pain was awful, infection likely or else the patient died of shock or loss of blood. Apart from that, they could offer some comforting words and just wait for the patient to

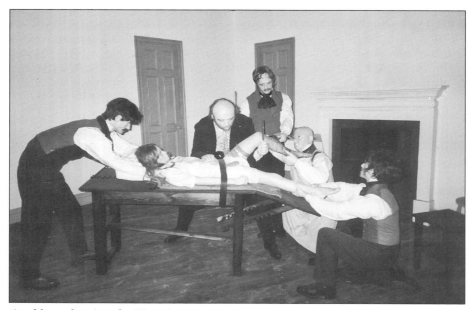

A tableau showing the Victorian surgeon preparing to amputate. Speed was essential – 9 seconds or death would follow. (By kind permission of the Thackray Medical Museum, Leeds)

improve: or otherwise. Much that was done actually prevented people from getting better.

With so little real medical knowledge, is it any wonder that charlatans and quacks flourished with promises of wonder cures. Such a one was Mary Bateman, the Yorkshire Witch hanged at York in 1809. Born near Thirsk in 1768, she married a Leeds man and by 1806 had acquired a reputation as a wise woman, fortune teller, thief and fraudster. Unsuspecting Rebecca Perigo of Bramley, Leeds asked Mary for help with an illness she believed was the result of a curse. Over the next ten months Rebecca and her husband gave Mary everything they owned but still no cure. Finally Mary made a poisoned pudding which killed Rebecca. Mary was convicted at York Assizes in March 1809 and a large crowd came to see the hanging.

Mary Bateman's body was returned to Leeds for display, raising £30 for the General Infirmary. It was then dissected by a surgeon during an anatomy course, raising yet more money from the fees charged to the medical students. A rather dubious way to make money!

Life was short and not very sweet. In 1841 life expectancy in Leeds was 25 years for the labouring poor. Even Yorkshire gentry could only expect to live to 52. If childbirth did not kill you a woman could expect to live two years longer than a man. A labourer in York had eight years less life than a working man in the country. You might work long arduous hours in harsh weather conditions but you were better off living on the Moors, the East Coast or the Dales – unless you were a lead miner. You stood little chance of a long healthy life in an industrial town with the overcrowding, pollution, and dangerous working conditions.

The Reverend John Wesley tried to help with his *Primitive Physic* first published in 1747. He was an Anglican clergyman who together with his brother Charles founded the Methodist movement. Concerned with the underprivileged, he wrote *Primitive Physic* for ordinary people to better their social and medical conditions. 'It is my design to set down cheap, safe and easy medicines, easily to be known, easy to be procured, and easy to be applied by plain unlettered men.' The profits from his hugely popular book went towards the maintenance of Methodist preachers in the industrial parishes, the deep countryside and the hill country of Yorkshire.

Surgery at the beginning of the 20th century was made slightly less grim by anaesthesia which was often administered by a porter holding a rag and a bottle of chloroform. It was all very hit and miss as the chloroform was likely to kill you by stopping the heart for good.

Antiseptic procedures were used in the form of carbolic soap but the avoidance of contamination during the operation was not fully understood. Operations were performed quickly in order that the

Mary Bateman – the Yorkshire Witch. Found guilty at York Assizes in 1809 and hanged. (By kind permission of the Thackray Medical Museum, Leeds)

patient would not bleed to death but also with much theatrical flourish as the surgeon enjoyed playing to an audience. Often the poor patient was reduced to a stage prop for the great man's showmanship.

Before the National Health Service in 1948 General Practioners set up in practice, 'putting up a plate' where they felt they could earn a living, and worked from surgeries in their own houses with a minimum amount of equipment and dispensing their own medicines. Not all were like the large Irishman who ministered to the people of Terrington, near Castle Howard. He visited on horseback, riding over fields and hedges and if the family could not pay him he would cheerfully say, 'Don't worry if you can't pay, the Lord will'.

Prior to 1948, patients who were weekly wage earners paid to be on a doctor's 'panel' and were treated free of charge. Others paid a fee as and when they became seriously ill. People thought twice before going to see a doctor and it was common practice to consult others before venturing to the surgery.

It comes as a shock to realise, until 60 years ago, just how little physicians could do for their patients. Is it any wonder that most sensible Yorkshire people tried to keep their loved ones out of the clutches of the

The reconstructed doctor's dispensary, originally used by Dr Isaac Bainbridge of Brough in Cumbria in the early 1900s. (Ann Holubecki, by kind permission of the Dales Countryside Museum at Hawes)

medical profession? Cures that appeared to work were jotted down by women in their 'commonplace' book or passed on by word of mouth. Men too took an interest and at the back of many an old household or farm accounts book the odd remedy was recorded: mostly for livestock – cows and sheep were worth money.

Living in a town you often had access to a herbalist and chemists made up medicines at your request. Opium was widely used in popular remedies and many chemists made up their own brand of laudanum. Huge quantities of 'opiates' were sold and could be found in anything from cough medicines to babies' teething syrups.

Country people gathered free from nature – nettles, dock leaves, dandelions, burdock, hawthorn, rose hips, elderberries – and made their own medicine.

Many concocted a remedy from the contents of the kitchen cupboard: vinegar, bread, onions, treacle, sugar and butter. All families believed that the cornerstone of good health rested in the regular evacuation of the bowels. Little self-help remedy books were sold from door to door covering everything from 'Ankles – weak' to 'Worms – to Destroy'. One such book advised very strongly that 'the prospect of doctors is becoming worse yearly, and are often more to be feared than the disease.'

Ordinary men and women did their best for their families. Now we can pop a pill, but in the past there was just human ingenuity, the hedgerow, the contents of the kitchen cupboard and as a last resort – the doctor.

SHORT, SHARP AND NOT PARTICULARLY SWEET

'41.6 per cent of the people born, die before attaining the age of 6 years.'
Report to the General Board of Health on Haworth in the
West Riding, 1850.

Anyone interested in social history must visit the splendid Thackray Medical Museum in Leeds. The interactive galleries and exhibitions illuminate the grim medical history and life of Victorian Leeds and other industrial towns. Diseases now unheard of stalked the stinking alleyways and ravaged the working poor. Cholera, typhoid and dysentery all took a toll on people living without proper sanitation and drinking water. Smallpox with its pus-filled blisters killed

The Thackray Medical Museum, Beckett Street, Leeds. Open Tuesday to Sunday. Originally the Leeds Union Workhouse, the splendid facade and entrance hall hid the grim reality behind. (Ann Holubecki)

many or left them scarred for life. National epidemics of influenza killed off the vulnerable made weak by malnutrition and awful working conditions.

Almost half the deaths in the 1840s were of children under five. It was a sad and desperate part of life that you would expect to lose a child to illnesses that are now treatable and which, if the living conditions had been more sanitary, would never have occurred in the first place. People lived in a state of fear and resignation.

Beechams Pills can be helpful for many things but this unashamed playing on parental fears in the *Graphic* magazine of 1890 takes some beating:

> A little child lay on her bed of pain,
> With deep blue eyes and wealth of golden hair,
> Longing that summer hours would come again
> With all their sunshine and their pleasure fair.
>
> With ministry of quiet tender love
> The mother watched beside her as she lay.
> A message came – O joy, all joys above!
> It turned her sadness into brightest day.
>
> It told of certain cure – what words of cheer
> For weary sickness and all mortal ills!
> Returning health soon blessed the child so dear,
> Who gladly took a box of 'BEECHAMS PILLS'.

TUBERCULOSIS

In the 1850s tuberculosis caused one in six deaths in Britain. Everyone knew the symptoms: coughing, fever, weakness, weight loss and the dread sight of blood coughed up in the sputum. Tuberculosis spreads by breathing in infected droplets and rich or poor, all were susceptible. Where people were living in badly ventilated rooms whole families were struck down.

The most famous consumptives in Yorkshire must be the Brontë family in the vicarage at Haworth. Haworth was one of the most unhealthy places to live in the 1800s, comparable with the worst districts of London. Maria, Elizabeth, Emily and Anne all died of the disease. Anne was sent off to Scarborough to try a sea cure but died there after a few days. The only brother Patrick Branwell, already weakened by an addiction to alcohol and opium, probably also had TB although his death certificate said 'Chronic Bronchitis Marasmus'. Only Charlotte seems to have escaped. Her death certificate in 1855 recorded 'Phthisis', the wasting away brought on by tuberculosis, but it is thought now that her death was more likely caused by *hyperemesis gravidarum* – excessive morning sickness.

There was no effective treatment for consumption, as it was known, until the 1940s with the discovery of streptomycin, the testing of all dairy herds for TB and the pasteurising of milk.

Public Health notices warned:

> If you see a neighbour spit
> Let the warden know of it
> On this matter please be firm
> Handkerchiefs will stop that germ.

Fresh air and nourishing food were seen as the only cures. An article on the prevention of consumption in the Hawes Church Magazine, 1911 recommended building an open air shelter. 'The patient who is not able to work should spend all his time in the open air shelter, not going indoors for his meals if this can be avoided. Nothing less than 8 hours in the open air daily can be considered as satisfactory. Bread, treacle, dripping, jam, figs, currants, raisins are all nourishing. Tripe, brain, liver

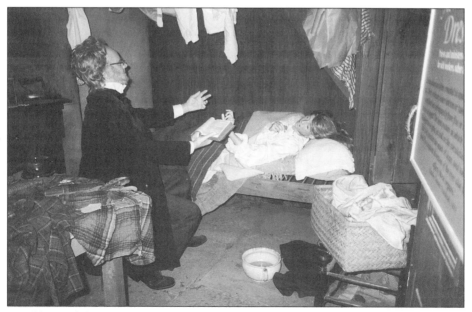

A tableau of the suffering poor. A young consumptive being comforted by the clergy.
(Ann Holubecki, by kind permission of the Thackray Medical Museum, Leeds)

and kidney are cheap and nutritious. The custom many patients have of drinking port wine because it is strengthening, can only be regarded as a bad one.'

For tuberculosis you were sent to the sanatorium for fresh air, sleeping in cold conditions 'outdoors'. Killingbeck Hospital in Leeds was the TB hospital. When mother was admitted the children went into a home.

Grace Handley, Settle

There were several isolation hospitals round Sheffield. The one in Crimaka Lane was for TB. It was burned down in 1960 to prevent any contagious diseases that might be lying dormant from reinfecting. TB was a killer and very much on people's minds. If you sat on the bus and someone started coughing you moved away.

Mac Webster, Sheffield

Old remedies for tuberculosis included swallowing live snails to eat the phlegm off your chest. Of course this was absurd but snails are nutritious and might help a weakened patient.

Rosemary to strengthen the patient. This herb acted as a tonic.

Ginger to strengthen the circulation and help reduce fever and coughing.

Lobelia inflata (also known as pukeweed) was much used as a stimulant, emetic, expectorant and relaxant.

Thackray Medical Museum, Leeds

Snail soup drunk for the cure for consumption and the skin of an eel (skinned when alive) placed in a silken bag and worn so as to rest on the chest is believed to cut phlegm.

Bedale book of Witchcraft 1773

A cure for consumption from an Otley medical practice dated 1875. 'Commence with a wash down in a morning with vinegar and salt with a little cayenne for night sweats. An emetic of lobelia once or twice in the week according to the strength of the patient. Then take …' the remedy goes on with a list of highly detailed and in parts illegible ingredients which included 2 ounces of mouse ear!

Joyce Banks, Yeadon

DIPHTHERIA

Diphtheria was another major killer until the launch of an immunisation campaign in 1940, which virtually eliminated the disease. Starting with a sore throat and fever, caused by bacteria in coughs and sneezes, a membrane could grow across the throat making breathing difficult. The toxins led to heart failure and paralysis of the muscles for breathing and swallowing. It was most common in autumn and winter and mainly afflicted children.

I was born in 1922 and had a grandma who was a great helper of Dr Touman of Stokesley. As a child I suffered many of the remedies of both my grandma and mother. One I remember vividly whenever there was a diphtheria epidemic was coming home from school and having to stand over a fire shovel of red hot coals, which was sprinkled with yellow sulphur powder. We children had to open our mouths and inhale the fumes the best we could. In my case it must have helped but both my brother and sisters eventually had to go in the 'Fever Van' to West Lane Hospital, Middlesbrough, along with other children who had contracted the disease.

A.T., Voss, Norway

SCARLET FEVER

A highly contagious disease spread by physical contact and germ laden air. Large families in overcrowded rooms led to ideal conditions for epidemics. It is a streptococcal infection so before the introduction of antibiotics all that could be done was to try and reduce the fever and isolate the patient.

The blue ambulance was the fever ambulance. People suffering from scarlet fever and diphtheria would be moved to Lodge Moor outside Sheffield. People would keep away from the street where the sick person lived for a week. When you visited you stood on a verandah and waved at the patient through the window. It was very, very cold up there. People wore iodine lockets in Sheffield. They were supposed to stop you getting scarlet fever and diphtheria and they smelt terrible.

Mac Webster, Sheffield

If you had seen someone with scarlet fever you gargled with salt water –
a teaspoon to a pint.

Muriel Dinsdale, Carperby

Emily Brontë hated the medical profession and referred to them as 'Poisoning Doctors', but there were several herbs used by medical men and herbalists that might have helped in these life threatening illnesses. It was believed elderflower tea raised the blood to the surface and brought out the poisons of the disease. Anything to increase sweating helped to reduce body temperature in a fever. Meadowsweet was given to soothe pain and inflammation and this plant contains an aspirin-like substance which would help. Hyssop was also known for its soothing properties and is used in modern medicine to clear phlegm.

Applying boiled turnips to the feet of a smallpox victim seems strange to us now but it was a common remedy for fevers and infection and the evaporating

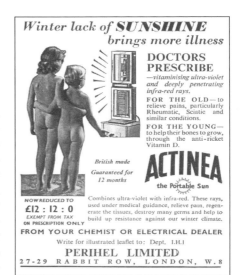

In 1956 children were still needing an extra boost to their systems. Rickets caused growing bones to soften and become malformed and was brought on by poor diet and lack of vitamin D.

sweat would cool the fever. Sulphur when burned produces sulphurous acid gas which was widely used as a disinfectant. Emily Brontë may have been a little harsh in her judgement but on the whole the medical men were powerless when faced with the desperately sick.

GETTING IT OFF YOUR CHEST

'When north-east winds prevail, make free use of toast and water, drink very hot, sweetened well with brown sugar candy which acts on the lungs.' Advice from An Old Corner Cupboard.

I received more remedies for coughs than any other ailment and the reason for this is fairly obvious.

In industrial towns people lived in a pall of perpetual smoke and pollution from factories, furnaces, steam engines and homes belching out fumes from coal fires. Housing was cramped, damp and badly ventilated with families living in crowded smokey conditions. Many jobs carried serious health risks to the lungs: miners, quarry workers, textile workers, ship builders; even farm workers in the fresh air were at risk from Farmer's Lung from the spores of fungus in mouldy hay or straw.

Only after the Great London Smog of 1952 when many people died was something done. The Clean Air Act in 1956 had a great impact not only on the health of town dwellers but also the appearance of the buildings, which had been blackened with soot over the years.

Cigarette smoking was hugely popular, advertisements encouraging you to smoke 'for your throat's sake'. The lungs took a beating and frequently objected in the form of a cough: a bout of bronchitis was normal during the winter months.

In the 1930s I can remember as a schoolgirl my mother making a very nice cough mixture. Wash a turnip well, cut it into round slices and then into a large basin start off with a slice of turnip and then a layer of brown sugar. Continue these alternate layers until the basin was full, then cover with a plate and one of the old fashioned flat irons to act as a weight. The basin was put into the warm oven at the side of the fire and left until the sugar had melted into the turnip juice. It made a delicious cough mixture.

J.K. Thompson, Beverley

The juice from turnips soaked in brown sugar was a lovely drink. My daughter loved it and used to suck the slices of turnip – it helped children through whooping cough.

May Dinsdale, Thornbury

Audrey Bailey of Thoralby about to demonstrate how to make the turnip cough medicine for a short piece on my search for old cures broadcast by Tyne Tees Television.

In my youth I suffered from bronchitis and my mother's cure was to cut a large peeled onion in half, placing it on a saucer and covering it in sugar. After a while a thick syrup formed in the saucer and I was given a tablespoon of this mixture at regular intervals. The taste and smell were beyond description.

D. Chapman, Hornsea

This is from the 'common book' of my grandma Bertha Clarke who lived in Barnsley and ran a little shop from the front room of her house selling home-made cakes, bread and pork pies. She was married in 1891 and by 1904 had five children. Grandfather, a lay Reader, worked for the local doctor, book-keeping and collecting weekly payments from patients. For a good cough remedy mix 3 fresh eggs, 4 ounces of honey, half a pint of port wine and 3 tablespoons of rum.

Margaret May, Almondbury

For chest infections in babies a cinder was taken from the fire and placed in a cup of water. When it had cooled down a drop of the cinder water was given to the baby on a spoon. It was called sulphur water and this was done regularly where I lived.

R. Bray, Cleckheaton

Rub chest with camphorated oil or apply hot poultice, take 3 drops essence of camphor in milk every hour. Taken from a *Book for Every Home.*

Colin Chippindale, Great Horton

From my mother's handwritten book amongst the list of clothes she took for us on holiday. For cough syrup take 1 tablespoon each of castor oil, vinegar and golden syrup. Mix well and take half a teaspoon. Who would dare cough after taking this!

Nora Shuttleworth, Birkenshaw

That doyen of doctors, Dr Pickles from Aysgarth, always gave me rose hip syrup for a cough in the 1920s.

John Terry, Marske

Author's note – Dr Will Pickles was a country doctor with a surgery in Aysgarth in Wensleydale. From this quiet and isolated dale he became world famous for research into all kinds of epidemic illnesses, particularly their incubation periods. He published *Epidemiology in Country Practice* in 1939.

My grandmother, Granny Myatt came from the West Riding. Born in 1855, she had a hard life and as a young widow worked to support her three children and her widowed mother. She could not afford medical help and soon became known as the local 'wise woman' for remedies. The local doctor recommended his poorer patients to her when he knew they could not pay. All her family did well and she died at the age of 78, a good age in those days. Granny Myatt's Cough Cure – half a pint of water, 1 teaspoon vinegar, 1 tablespoon Golden Syrup, 2 ounces butter, 1 lb brown sugar. Put all in a pan and keep boiling till all sugar melted and 'it tastes right'. When tested in cold water it makes a soft ball. Suck this until your tongue is sore and the cough will be gone. (No remedy found for sore tongues!) Granny Myatt's mother, great grandma Simpson's recipe for a sore chest. If the patient, especially a child is wheezing and having difficulty breathing, warm a cup of milk and stir in 1 teaspoon of Golden Syrup and 2 teaspoons of grated suet. Stir well and drink while warm. Granny Myatt would not use this revolting stuff unless the suet was left out.

Hilda Jackson, Bedale

My mother's recipe for cough mixture back in the 1920s was 2 pennyworth each of Spanish juice (liquorice), oil of almonds, peppermint, aniseed and paregoric. Some white wine vinegar and 1 lb treacle. Dissolve the Spanish juice in a pint of boiling water. Add the treacle and stir well. When cool add all other ingredients and bottle.

E. Grayson, Sheffield

Author's note – the above remedy was a very commonly used one and I received it in slightly different forms from across the county, sometimes the white wine vinegar was left out.

For coughs my mother would boil liquorice sticks slowly with linseed oil. Ugh!
Peppermint essence and honey in hot water.

Eileen Crabtree, Ramsgill

Make a mustard plaster by mixing mustard powder with water and put onto a wool flannel and then place on the back for a chesty cough or pleurisy. A rabbit skin could be worn against the chest for extra warmth.

Muriel Dinsdale, Carperby

My mother was a great believer in turpentine. Two drops on a lump of sugar for a chesty cough.

Eleanor Dinsdale, Carperby

During the war years for a cough granny used to give us a mixture of 3 lumps of mint rock, bought in a sweetshop, covered with butter and 4 dashes of vinegar. Let it melt in the oven of the old kitchen range.

Brenda Marsh, Hull

Boil some onions, mix with bread and milk and season with salt and pepper. Very good for a bad chest and temperature.

Annie Alexander, Hull

Three tablespoons each of whisky and honey, 2 dessertspoons of glycerine, the juice of 2 lemons, shake all together and take a dessertspoon at a time.

E. Oliver, Burstwick

My great-grandmother came from Osgodby and was known as 'The Osgodby Venus' due to her extraordinary beauty. She passed on to her daughter, my grandmother Alice Johnson, some of her remedies. Alice came from Carleton near Skipton and lived to the grand age of 99. From her herb notes comes help for a persistent

A 1931 advertisement for Chlorodyne, once used as a cure-all.

cough. Try a big spoonful of honey in coltsfoot tea. Use coltsfoot leaves in the teapot instead of tea.

Fox Johnson, Saltaire

If you had a bad cold you went to the chemist for a tuppenny bottle of chlorodyne mixed with liquorice and ipecacuanha wine. However, people bought the chlorodyne separately, diluted it and used it as cheap alcohol so you cannot get it anymore.

Mac Webster, Sheffield

Oil of almonds and syrup of violets with squills was good for nasty coughs.

Tallow fat and nutmeg spread onto a flannel, made as hot as possible and used as a poultice on the chest of anyone with bronchitis.

Flowers of sulphur blown down the throat to ease 'dry lungs'.

Catharine M. Parker, Threshfield

Joyce Banks of Yeadon came across some interesting remedies when researching the history of the Otley medical practice where she works. Little could be done to alleviate the cause of the cough in Victorian times but here the doctor was not too proud to jot down anything that a patient or colleague might recommend.

'From Israel Burnett of Hartshead Moor near Cleckheaton 1877.

Dear Sir, I understand from my daughter that you want a Prescription of mine for a cough. 1 dessert spoonful each of oatmeal and honey, some Butter (about the size of a wallnut [sic]), 1 fresh egg and a little salt. Mix these as a paste then pour 1 pint of boiling water on the above. Drink 1 pint per day.'

For a Cough or Cold related by Mr Barker 1881 – '1 pennyworth each of Dandelion and Ground Ivy to be put into 3 pints of water and boiled down to a pint. Dose a wineglassful 3 times a day.'

PNEUMONIA

Good for pneumonia: Half a noggin of brandy, 3 pennyworth of Saffron. Dissolve for 24 hours and take 1 teaspoon 3 times a day.

Nora Shuttleworth, Birkenshaw

My sister had pneumonia in the 1930s and the only treatment in those days was a bread poultice put between a bit of gauze and placed on the chest. Later you used kaolin (white china clay) instead of the bread. You got the patient into the kitchen and had all the pans boiling to create steam to help the breathing. Another time Uncle Jack had pneumonia and came to us to be nursed by my mother. When she went out, another aunt, not medically minded, came round to keep an eye on him. She heated the kaolin and put this onto the gauze and then straight onto the chest, without a barrier of gauze between the kaolin and the chest. When it dried it had stuck to his very hairy chest and nothing would get it off. Father had to use his cut-throat razor and shave Uncle's chest!

Mac Webster, Sheffield

Years ago when the children were little my son developed a croup-like cough. My neighbour's old mother was visiting her and heard him coughing. She came round and insisted on making him a 'pneumonia jacket'. This was made from a roll of cotton wool, cut into two pieces and held by safety pins. First she lathered the child's chest and back with Vick and lard, I didn't have any goose fat in, seeing as it was 1960 and not 1860! Then the vest was applied. Every morning I had to cut an inch strip off the bottom until it was all gone. She said, 'For Heaven's sake don't remove it all at once or he will go into shock.' Silly me carried out the instructions to the letter as she insisted on checking the vest every day. PS: He's still living and now 38!

Liz Brooke, Otley

Would any of the above remedies have done you any good? Paregoric was used extensively and helped to deaden pain and make you drowsy. Not surprising when you consider it contained opium, benzoic acid, camphor, aniseed oil and proof spirit. Most of the ingredients in these remedies like liquorice, cod liver oil, glycerine, Golden Syrup, sugar and honey would act as a lubricant and perhaps soothe the cough. A little drop of alcohol would certainly make you feel more relaxed without actually doing you any good medicinally.

The sulphur water made with a cinder from the fire is an interesting remedy. British coal had a high sulphur content, hence the pollution and smogs which were so much a part of townspeople's lives. When taken internally it has certain disinfectant properties but is principally known for its effectiveness as a laxative.

Ipecacuanha is the root of a Brazilian shrub and was found in many cough medicines. In small doses it acts as a stimulant to the respiratory passages and liquifies the thick mucous which occurs in bronchitis.

The application of a poultice to the chest was not likely to help much apart from giving comfort to the patient who would feel something was being done. However, the heat could relieve the pain felt on coughing or drawing breath.

Ground ivy has a tonic effect on the bronchial system and is an expectorant and coupled with dandelion would be a powerful diuretic. Saffron stimulates the circulation and increases perspiration. Mustard used externally causes increased blood flow and removal of toxins but too much will leave the skin blistered. Coltsfoot leaves can be eaten in salads and relax spasms and control coughing: the Osgodby Venus was on to something. A squill is any flower of the Scilla plant, especially the sea onion found in the Mediterranean and is a powerful expectorant but too much is poisonous as shown by the fact it was once an ingredient of rat poison!

Camphor should never be ingested and pharmacists would always advise caution and sensible use. It is now recognised as a powerful substance, an excess of which can cause poisoning and even death. Caring mothers who rubbed camphorated oil onto their children's chests and made them wear camphor lockets round the neck to ward off coughs and colds, little realised that they were in grave danger of poisoning their loved ones. Those readers who remember as a child being treated in this way may well pause to reflect just how lucky they are to be around still.

Sung in school playgrounds throughout Yorkshire to the tune of *John Brown's Body*.

> John Brown's baby's got a cold upon its chest,
> John Brown's baby's got a cold upon its chest,
> John Brown's baby's got a cold upon its chest –
> And they rubbed it with camphorated oil.
> Cam-phor-am-phor-am-phor-aaaated.
> Cam-phor-am-phor-am-phor-aaaated
> Cam-phor-am-phor-am-phor-aaaated –
> And they rubbed it with camphorated oil!

THE GLORIOUS GOOSE

*'For chesty colds we had goose grease well rubbed into chest and back.
It was also good for the leather tops of our clogs.'*
Henry T. Charlton, Hull.

Was there ever such a golden bird as the goose? At one time every family who could afford it would have sat down to a goose at Christmas time. The delicious meat would have yielded great quantities of fat in the cooking which was then carefully preserved in jars for further medical use. Other bits were never wasted for a goose wing proved useful for cleaning the chimney and the feathers to stuff pillows and mattresses.

However, would you consider a goose wing as a medical instrument? Back in the 1930s Dr Dunbar of Wensleydale visited a farmer's wife who was having trouble with retention of urine. She lived in a remote part of the dale and it was a long walk to return to the surgery in Aysgarth for a catheter. Seeing some geese in the yard the good doctor called for a goose quill which he adapted, boiled and then used to give the poor lady some relief.

For most people their medical use of the goose was confined to a spoonful of goose grease for croup and rubbing the stuff onto the chest and back before carefully covering with brown paper, red flannel, vest or liberty bodice. Goose grease was a powerful insulator of heat. Keeping warm was regarded as most important in the fight against infection; you and those who passed within your orbit had to put up with the smell.

Whitby fishermen had another use for it. Goose fat was melted with gorse flowers to make Yorkshire Goose Salve which healed hands cracked by salt water and cold. It was also good for gardeners as the gorse healed cuts and thorn wounds.

The goose has become neglected over the years. The efficacy of goose grease is known only to those over a certain age and our modern sensibilities no longer allow us to mix in company smelling of goose fat. However, just how far we have come from our recent past is revealed in the story I received from Ken Tyers of Consett in Co Durham. I know this book is about Yorkshire but the story is too good to be left out.

'As a schoolboy in the 1930s I was brought up by my grandmother who was a widow. She was the mother of twelve children but in the early Thirties only four were still at home, plus two grandchildren and herself. With a regular income of only 10 shillings (50 pence in today's money) we had to use home remedies. Grandmother's cures must have worked on me as I was 20 years old when I first visited a doctor and that was as a result of a pit accident. Grandmother always used goose grease for chest colds.

Years later a young woman asked me if I could get her some goose grease as her mother wanted some. I said I would but it would have to wait until the farmer killed his geese at Christmas. This young lady was very upset at this, saying, "I didn't know you had to kill the goose first to get the fat!"'

WHOOPING COUGH

'At Scarborough some owners of the seaside donkeys earned income in the winter by charging whooping cough victims for rides, as it was thought to be a remedy.' Thackray Medical Museum, Leeds.

Mothers dreaded the childhood illness of whooping cough. Spread by droplets breathed out by the infected child, it would spread through a family in no time. Immunization against whooping cough started in the mid 1950s but before that every family could expect a dose. The hacking cough develops into a distinctive 'whoop' noise which is the drawing in of breath at the end of a coughing spasm. It was a distressing illness often with vomiting after the coughing, with the further complication of pneumonia never far away. Desperate mothers turned to superstition and unconventional cures – it was all they had.

Pass a child with whooping cough under a donkey's belly.

Thackray Medical Museum, Leeds

For the chin-cough or whooping cough. Rub the feet thoroughly with hog's lard before the fire, at going to bed, and keep the child warm.

Swallow four wood lice alive in a spoonful of jam or treacle and the 'whoop' will vanish.

John Wesley's 'Primitive Physic'

A field mouse skinned and made into a small pie then eaten, the warm skin bound hair-side against the throat, and kept there for nine days will cure the worst whooping cough.

Catch a frog, open its mouth then cough into it three times, then throw the frog over your left shoulder for luck.

The Bedale Witchcraft book of 1773

The people of the North York Moors were highly superstitious and the place-names of Hob Cross, Hob Dale, Hob Hill show a strong belief in the benefactions of the local Hobs. These goblins were often attached to a particular place or family. They were believed to be small, hairy, rather ugly and preferred a solitary life doing small tasks around the farm for no

Runswick Bay with the Hob Holes at the bottom of the cliffs at the far side of the bay.

reward. As they often went naked we have to suppose that it was a good thing they were never seen.

The Runswick Hob lived in a cave known as Hob Hole on the shores of Runswick Bay. He was reputed to be able to cure whooping cough or kink-cough as it was known locally. The child was taken to the mouth of the cave and there the mother would plead for help.

> 'Hob Hole Hob,
> Ma bairn's gotten t'kink-cough,
> Tak it off, tak it off!'

Belief in Hobs waned by the 1900s but a similar cure was still being used well into the last century. The only remedy available to anxious Teeside mothers and grandmothers, which appeared to work, was to wrap up the child and take them down to the seaside when the tide was right out. It was most effective at Spring tide with the highest high tide and the lowest low tide. Together they walked out to the water's edge when the tide was right out at extreme low tide and recited: 'Bairn's got kink-cough, Tak't off, tak't off.'

This was said more than once and then they would walk back slowly as the tide turned and the sea came in. This ritual took place on the wide stretch of sand between Redcar and Saltburn and I was told this was still being done up until 1948.

Anxious parents stood at the entrance to these forbidding Hob Holes on Runswick Bay to ask the Hob to cure their children of whooping cough.

Other cures involving fresh air took place when a child with whooping cough was taken onto the moors for the day to try and rid the sufferer of the 'whoop'. A hole was cut into the turf and the child's mouth held close to the freshly dug earth to breathe in the smell which was believed to effect a cure. There was some common sense in this combination of fresh air and getting the child away from the rest of the family to stop the spread of infection.

I was mollycoddled as a child in the 1950s so when I went to school I caught everything. When I was about six I caught whooping cough and was very ill for some time and it left me with a nasty cough. Mother used to drag me round the streets of Bradford looking for places where they were boiling up the tar to tarmac the road. I had to stand there and inhale it. I was left very thin and with no appetite and in those days if you had too much time off school the School Board man came round to investigate you. Bradford Corporation had a place at Manor Row for children who were sickly. I went on a Monday morning and there would be a dozen of us stripped to the waist sat in this room having 'sun ray'

treatment. Five minutes on your front then a bell rang and you turned round and had five minutes on your back. Our immune systems were deficient and this was an attempt to give us some vitamin D.

Carol Simpson, Eccleshill

My mother lived in Middlesbrough and my father was a tug boat skipper. The night soil was taken out into the river Tees on barges and dumped into the sea. Children with whooping cough were often taken out on the barge to breathe in the methane gas!

Dulcie Jones, Great Ayton

There is a long held belief in the curative properties of the pungent odour of ozone at the seaside. Dr Lucy Carpenter of York University, an expert on these matters, explained that at Spring tide when the whooping cough ritual took place, the seaside smell at most beaches is at its strongest. The odour can be quite similar to that of ozone and this has been a popular myth since the Victorian era. However, the smell of the seaside is much more likely to be that of iodine and bromine, both of which are naturally present in the ocean in small concentrations and emanate from living seaweeds in large concentrations. Seaweeds are exposed to air at Spring low tide. The good effect of the seaside to the afflicted children was probably due to them simply inhaling fresh air free from the toxic pollutants back home.

THOSE WERE THE DAYS

We never used to lock the doors, our neighbours we could trust,
If someone had not been seen all day a visit was a must.
Whatever ailment one did have someone knew a cure;
A long tried remedy handed down, renewed good health was sure.
Cinder tea for stomach pains, pennyroyal for women's ills.
If one felt really upset, you took a little liver pill.
Brimstone and treacle to assist the motions, Turkey rhubarb for a stubborn case.
Permanganate of potash for irritant spots on the face.
Mothers chased the tar sprayer on the road for children with whooping cough,
Making them stand in acrid fumes, kids in those days were tough.
Brown paper with goose grease was placed on the front of a youngster with a weak chest;
The smell was enough to suffocate them, like a well used poultry nest!
A soap and sugar poultice for an abcess or boil,
Until the thing came to a head, the sight made one recoil.
Senna pod for the weekly drink, just prior to Sunday school
Although t'was most uncomfortable, it was within the rules.
Fullers Earth for nappy rash, a fine tooth comb for nits,
A tepid bath for a fractious child or one who was having fits.
Marshmallow and comfrey for painful strains, paregoric for a cough.
Cold key down the back for a bleeding nose, the shock made one take off.
Hot treacle, marge and vinegar for irritant of the throat.
A cobweb placed on a nasty cut, or the hair of an old goat.
Friars Balsam and steam for a blocked up nose; raw onion for thinning hair.
Spreading spittle on a nasty wart; a shade for a cross-eyed stare.
Everyone had their favourite cure, expensive or just plain muck.
Faith was the healer in those hard days: or was it just good luck!

My father wrote this when we were children – I am now 82.

M. Butler, Maltby

COLD COMFORT

'Always set your face firmly towards health. Say that you are better when people enquire; the very declaration will assist in making you feel so.' Wensleydale and Swaledale Almanack, 1914.

We have all suffered the common cold: the awful blocked nose, swollen sinuses, sore throat and general feeling of misery. A highly contagious virus infection, a sufferer just has to 'tough it out' and hope it does not lead to anything worse.

My father Clifford Watson, who is now in his late eighties, was born in Smeaton. Like many families they cured their own bacon. He remembered as a child if you had a cold, a slice of fatty bacon was cut off the joint and made into a bacon plaster by putting the bacon between two pieces of cloth. It was then attached to tapes and put on the chest. It kept the chest clear when you had a cold. Unfortunately if you were wearing this at school and it got warm the smell was awful.

My grandfather recommended vinegar in the bath if you felt a cold coming on.

Audrey Bailey, Thoralby

For a cold sprinkle castor oil onto brown paper and then grated nutmeg. Place brown paper onto chest and iron it on with a warm iron. Place your vest over the top to keep the paper in place.

Muriel Dinsdale, Carperby

Yeast, sugar and butter mixed into a paste for a cold. Horrible!

Harold Hammond, Askrigg

Eat boiled onions for a cold, it gets the mucous membranes flowing.

Sheila Fawcett, West Witton

My mother died when I was seven and for a time we had a housekeeper who came from the West Riding. My sister and I were mortified when she made little bags to hold a piece of camphor. This was attached with ribbons round our neck and we were supposed to wear this all winter to ward off colds.

Denny Minnitt, Askrigg

Hips and haws – nature's bounty. The rose hip is a tonic herb, rich in vitamins. As a child in the 1950s I remember picking rose hips from the hedgerow and taking them to the collecting point at the village post office and being paid. The hawthorn has been used since the Middle Ages as a heart remedy.

If anyone came into the house with a cold my sister-in-law would cut an onion in two. Half would go on a saucer in the living room, the other half on the window-ledge in the bedroom. It stayed there until it was shrivelled up.

Mac Webster, Sheffield

I was one of six children, living in Huddersfield as a child. For a bad cold we would put a teaspoonful of mustard into a cup, mixed with sufficient milk to make a paste. Boil enough milk to fill the cup and add to paste and stir well. Go straight to bed with the drink and a hot-water bottle. It makes you sweat and I have had this many times and it works.

George Collings, Huddersfield

Blackcurrant tea to block the start of a cold.

Mustard in a footbath and a spoonful of mustard in black coffee is an overnight cure for 'flu and colds.

Catharine M. Parker, Threshfield

My mother Nancy Thomas of Otley had many old recipes handed down to her. Most she kept in her head but I was brought up with them. For colds and coughs equal parts of liquorice, chlorodyne and marsh-mallow. When I was a child in the 1950s it cost 9 old pence.

Hazel Layt, Alicante, Spain

For a cold a mixture of oil of amber, oil of cloves and camphorated oil rubbed on chest and inhaled.

Ann Holubecki, Redmire

This is from my mother's old Women's Institute book going back years. She made many of the remedies and lived to a great age. For coughs, colds and sore throats take 4 ounces of whole ginger, 1 quart of water and the rind of a lemon and boil together for 1 hour, then strain. To each pint of this liquid add 12 ounces of sugar and juice of a lemon. Boil for 10 minutes; skim well, bottle and seal for future use. For the dose put a small quantity in a glass and mix with boiling water.

Marjorie Wilson, Welton

I was at school during the Depression and times were hard in Bradford. For a cold, you bought raspberry vinegar from the chemist.

Mrs Nash, Allerton

A good cure for a cough or a cold in the head was hot water with a spoonful of mustard which you breathed in with a towel over your head. Hot lemonade was also supposed to be a good cure.

R. Bray, Cleckheaton

Taken from *A Book for Every Home* which included sections on home decorating, squeaking boots and the conjugation of French verbs! For a cold in the head smell eucalyptus oil. Eat gruel at night.

Colin Chippindale, Great Horton

To relieve an infant with nasal snuffles the soles of its feet were rubbed with the liquid from a garlic clove at bedtime. An older child could have a mashed clove in a muslin bag to wear round the neck.

Jean Booth, Sheffield

My great grandfather William Elston was a railwayman at the old Holbeck yard in Leeds. He was a Trade Unionist and his obituary stated he was 'an unassuming worker in the Labour cause.' He kept an accounts book from 1905 until he died in 1929 in which he wrote many remedies. How to cure a cold in one night. Boil 1 ounce of yarrow, half ounce of bruised ginger and 6 pennyworth of cayenne in 1 and a half pints of water, until reduced down to half pint. Take a wineglassful at bedtime. Spray 30 drops of eucalyptus oil in a pint of hot water and inhale for 10 minutes.

Susan Burnell, Swillington

Most people still have their pet remedies for treating a cold and most are harmless. A cold is self limiting – you are going to get better – but if something makes you feel more comfortable, as several of these ingredients obviously did, they are not curing it but making the symptoms more bearable.

Some of the ingredients in these cures could be surprisingly helpful in alleviating the misery of a cold. Onions are known to protect against infection. Dairy products promote secretions, as does ginger which has long been used in traditional medicines for coughs, colds and chills. Mustard, nutmeg and cloves are warming stimulants. Garlic has strong antibacterial properties and lowers fever by increasing perspiration. Eucalyptus is a good decongestant. Oil of amber is a form of pine oil and is considered by herbalists to be good for upper respiratory tract infections. Raspberry vinegar would have an astringent action.

Research into colds shows that hot spicy drinks and those mixing sweet and sour promote mucous secretions which are vital in the body's defences against bacteria and viruses.

According to a retired doctor friend, the old adage of 'feed a cold and starve a fever' is rubbish. On the whole a cold takes 3 days to come, 3 days with you, and 3 days to go away and this is still true today in spite of all our medical advances.

OWLER STAR'S HEALING WATERS

This story, as told to me by my late mother, is quite true and not an 'old wives' tale'. Frequently this treatment was used for colds in some south Yorkshire villages, for example Worrall and Oughtibridge.

Part way up the steep incline of a much grazed field which borders a country road with the strange name of Boggard Lane, near the village of Worrall near Sheffield, a spring bursts out of the hillside.

The ice-cold and crystal clear waters pour down into an ancient, hand-crafted and deep, roughly fashioned stone trough. When full, the waters, ever gathering momentum, rush down the hillside to join the river Don in the valley below.

Why Owler Star? This is thought to be the result of verbally passing

The Holy Well at Threshfield. Lady Well attracted pilgrims from far and wide as the waters were famous for healing many ailments. A mug is still chained to the wall for those wishing to drink the water.

The Old Wives' Well at Stape on the North Yorkshire moors. A rag well where visitors still bathe the part needing healing with a rag dipped in the water. The rag is then hung on a nearby bush and as it rots the healing supposedly occurs. Here is yours truly; an old wife bathing her poorly foot!

down the name through many, many years and that originally local folk named the spring 'Alder Spa', since many such trees grow in the area. It has always been believed that the waters contained 'medicinal' properties – iron, calcium, sulphur.

With such curative qualities country people – most very poor and unable to buy patent medicines anyway – believed that here were waters, free for the collecting – in buckets, saucepans, kettles, jugs – which when drunk or applied would cure all manner of diseases; from common colds to stomach aches, bowel disorders to fever. True? The mind can do all sorts of things.

Over many years hundreds of gallons of the water must have been collected from the trough by a constant procession of men and women, boys and girls.

My mother vividly remembered one 'cure' which had an immediate result, and this was for someone feeling very hot and feverish. Hot, sweating and having breathing problems, the sufferer lay upon a bed, probably just covered by a thin sheet, with bedroom windows wide open. It was furnished with typical simple furniture, a wooden chair and a dressing table upon which was a large pot washing bowl, with a jug beside it.

One of the children having been despatched a while ago with a bucket to collect some of Owler Star's water, returns and clomps up the wooden stairs, followed by the lady of the house. First, to detract attention from what was to happen, the patient was offered a glass of the water to drink, but warned to do so very slowly since the liquid was extremely cold.

Meanwhile the remainder of the bucketful was poured into the clean washbowl. Into this was then placed a sponge or flannel to soak in the water.

Having drunk their fill the patient put down the glass and enquired, 'What now?' Quickly, the covering sheet was removed and the sufferer exposed in nudity upon the bed. In a flash, the ice-cold cloth was – having been wrung out – swiftly brought down and pressed on the poor patient's tummy!

The effect was immediate. So shocked was the sufferer that there was an instant leap from the bed and a rush downstairs, holding the midriff, followed by a call from upstairs 'I knew that would cure you!' Few, 'tis said, returned to their bed after a 'dose' – one way or another – of Owler Star's healing waters.

Such remedies have long since been abandoned, but passing that spring – whose waters still pour down the same hillside – I think about those times.

Joe Castle, local historian, Sheffield

HEADACHE

'There is no commoner cause of troublesome headache than constipation together with close and prolonged confinement in overheated and badly ventilated rooms.' Advice to Edwardian ladies.

I was surprised to receive few cures for the universal headache, given the huge number of people who suffer from this debilitating condition. Perhaps a headache was thought of as trivial by our grandparents. I failed to find the word 'migraine' in any of the 'commonplace' and medical self-help books I examined. Are we less stoical now and is the pace of life in the 21st century proving to be a headache?

The boiled leaves of the feverfew plant for headaches.
June Stringfellow and Joyce Flynn, Pontefract

Vinegar on a handkerchief applied to the forehead.
Sheila McFarlane, Hebden Bridge

From *Old Fashioned Remedies* by the Swillington Methodist Ladies Bright Hour. For headaches from the heat place a cabbage leaf or a large lettuce leaf in your hat; it will keep the head cool.
Barbara Evans, Swillington

From *A Book for Every Home* a pinch of snuff or smelling salts will often remove a headache.
Colin Chippindale, Great Horton

From 'The Lady's World' 1898 – and what a world for some. Those in need of 'Bishop's Citrate of Caffeine' are businessmen, students and ladies of leisure who are 'prostrated by the excitement of shopping and sight-seeing.'

If troubled with a headache, try the simultaneous application of hot water to the feet and back of the neck.

Ann Holubecki, Redmire

Vinegar sponged onto the skin checks perspiration and produces coolness. A headache brought on by blocked sinuses might be jolted by a sharp whiff of smelling salts. Feverfew has long been known to be helpful in headaches and migraine, either to make tea with the leaves or chew on the raw leaf. However, the taste of the leaves is so horrible it is questionable which is worse, the headache or the cure.

EARACHE

'When ear troubles threaten, resource to the aural syringe will generally bring ease.' A 1930s 'Enquire Inside' book.

Such a delicate organ and yet what ferocious pain it can give. Earache is a common problem in young children and usually indicates infection behind the eardrum in the middle ear. However, many adults venturing out in a bitter north wind without hat or scarf suffer intense pain, only cured by getting back in the warm. As one gets older wax is often a problem, causing deafness. Earache and wax are now easily treated by a doctor, not so the other kind of hearing problem – male 'selective' deafness. If you live with someone suffering from this maddening affliction, you will know there is no cure apart from speaking louder!

★ ★ ★ ★ ★

Toasted bread put against the ear for earache.

Heather Peacock, Castle Bolton

Butcher Tom of Hawes gave my mother a cure for earache. Warm a drop of whisky on a spoon and drop it into the ear. It crackled and dissolved the wax.

Eleanor Dinsdale, Carperby

From my mother-in-law Katy Nolan's book of *600 Valuable Home Recipes*. For earache rub the ear well with a dry flannel or the ear should be bathed with a strong decoction of camomile flowers and poppy heads, as warm as it can be borne.

Mary Nolan, Stockton on Tees

Put a little lump of hot potato in ear.

June Stringfellow and Joyce Flynn, Pontefract

I was born in the early 1930s, the youngest of seven children, and I often had earache when I was young. I remember the middle of an onion warmed, put into my ear and a scarf to cover and yes, it did bring relief.

A. Smith, Sheffield

Dad would get a heap of salt on a spade or shovel and hold it over the fire to get very hot. Then it was tipped into one of his socks, tied up and held against the ear.

Margaret Brandon, Hebden Bridge

Warm olive oil rubbed onto the back of the ear and then wrap a scarf round the head.

Grace Handley, Settle

Warm olive oil dripped off a knitting needle into the ear.

Sheila McFarlane, Hebden Bridge

Warm a towel or a piece of flannelette sheeting in front of the fire and put it round the ear. When it got cool you had another one ready. It worked.

Mrs Roebuck, Sheffield

Ear-Ach from Cold. Boil Rue or Rosemary, or Garlick, [sic] and let the steam go into the ear thro' a funnel.

From The Reverend John Wesley's 'Primitive Physic'

From my mother's recipe book. She was a trained cook but took a job at the Grand Hotel, Scarborough as a ladies maid in the 1890s. If gnats or earwigs get into the ear, a puff of tobacco smoke will render them helpless and afterwards the ear can be rinsed with a little warm water.

Eileen Crabtree, Ramsgill

We are told now not to poke around in our ears for fear of damage and making matters worse but with what gusto the inside of the ear was treated in days gone by. Onion and garlic help protect against infection. Rosemary relaxes spasms and relieves pain and rue used externally is said by herbalists to help in earache but too much will cause blistering. John Wesley's idea to let the steam from these herbs into the ear might have been helpful. Most of these remedies were to do with warming the painful area, bringing comfort to the patient while waiting for the body's natural defences, the white blood cells, to fight the infection. As for insects in ears, it is to be most earnestly hoped that none of us ever suffer from such a visitation.

TOOTHACHE

'Two certain cures for toothache – either pulling out or driving further in.' Wensleydale Advertiser, 24th December 1844.

Hope springs eternal when it comes to toothache. Desperately we hope that on waking the next morning it will have gone away. We put off going to the dentist, for once in that reclining chair, our mouths wide open, we are at the mercy of someone wielding a drill. In days gone by fear and cost made us turn to alternative cures and some would say that not much has changed.

★ ★ ★ ★ ★

To chew on a clove would help take away the pain of toothache.
Sheila McFarlane, Hebden Bridge

From a *Book for Every Home.* For toothache, place a little scraped horseradish round the roots.
Colin Chippindale, Great Horton

From an *Old Corner Cupboard.* To cure toothache 1 teaspoonful each of ground ginger and Epsom salts, taken in a teacup of hot water.
June Ford, Brighouse

I was brought up on a farm at Piercebridge and remember having toothache treated by warm brown paper sprinkled with vinegar and pepper on it. It was lovely and soothing and I

In the 1900s a country doctor had to be a surgeon, dentist, optician and midwife. A collection of teeth successfully pulled by the doctor and kept as trophies? (Ann Holubecki, by kind permission of the Dales Countryside Museum at Hawes)

Not only were teeth extracted because of decay, many people routinely had all their teeth removed at an early age. Dental sepsis was seen as a cause of many illnesses including thrombosis and anaemia

always think of the rhyme Jack and Jill.

Olive Robinson, Darlington

Iodine on cotton wool for toothache.

Muriel Dinsdale, Carperby

For toothache my mother rubbed whisky on the tooth and gum.

Dulcie Lewis, Carperby

Make a poultice by scalding some oatmeal and place on a piece of muslin. Hold it to your face for toothache. You can also use this for drawing boils and carbuncles but have it hotter than you would for your face.

Lyn Cooper, Wyke

Oil of cloves or poppy heads were applied to the gums for toothache and gumboils.

E. Lynch, Pudsey

To prevent the Tooth-ache, rub the teeth often with Tobacco Ashes. Lay roasted parings of Turnips, as hot as may be, behind the ear. Wear round the neck a double hazel nut; this not only cures the complaint, but you will never suffer from the pain again.

A sheep's tooth in a bag will cure the Tooth-ache.

*The Reverend John Wesley's
'Primitive Physic'*

★ ★ ★ ★ ★

Den Chisholm from Marton near Middlesbrough, a Yorkshire dialect expert, told me of an old book published in Bedale in 1773 with cures, superstitions and witchcraft relating to health. Who can doubt the existence of the generous 'tooth fairy', but teeth have gathered some quite sinister folklore. According to this book, children's teeth must either be carefully preserved or utterly destroyed by fire with salt. Should one accidentally be swept away and fall into the ground or be buried by some evil minded person, the child will not live long. On the other hand a tooth found in a churchyard, and we can guess where it might have come from, is believed to charm away toothache if rubbed on the cheek.

TEETH CLEANING

Our teeth were brushed with soot from the chimney and a pinch of salt.
Jean Booth, Sheffield

Toothpaste was something we could not afford in my young days as I came from a family of nine. It was a case of putting the toothbrush up the chimney and using the soot as a cleanser. At my age I am fortunate in still having most of my own teeth.

Leonard Western, Sheffield

Bicarbonate of soda instead of toothpaste. Manufacturers have just caught up with this one as the new wonder toothpaste!
Catharine M. Parker, Threshfield

Toothache is a warning that something is wrong and only expert treatment can put it right. However, some of the remedies here might have temporarily eased the pain, most notably the cloves, ginger and the whisky. Heat as always is a great comforter. Tincture of iodine, once so liberally used, is no longer available as taken in large doses it is a violent irritant poison. Externally it was used as an antiseptic and many of us remember the intense pain of iodine dabbed onto a cut or graze. As for sheep's teeth and hazel nuts, not some of John Wesley's better remedies.

A DAY IN THE LIFE

I am the last of my family. My mother had 16 children but only 11 of us lived. You can imagine how it was when we were all at home. We all had our jobs to do. My eldest sister had the job of washing and cleaning the heads of the four youngest and giving us our medicine. She worked in the Metal Box factory in Hull and saw to us as soon as she came home from work and had her tea. She did this from the age of 14 until she got married at 27. My other three sisters all had jobs where they lived in. She called us in from playing, one at a time and washed us. Then with a small tooth comb cleaned our heads and then rubbed vinegar on our hair. Then we were given our brimstone and treacle and if we had a cough or cold we used to go to the chemist for 2 pennyworth of phenal and chlorodyne. We were all bathed in a tin bath in front of the fire with a handful of soda in the water. All my six brothers used liquid paraffin on their hair and we all had the best and thickest hair you could wish to see. We used Sunlight and Lifebuoy soap. My eldest sister died at 94 and she never took a tablet in her life and never ailed a thing.

Mary Sarel, Hull

THE INTERNAL WORKINGS

'It is a cardinal rule that the bowels should act once in every 24 hours. For treatment, regular habits should be enjoined, and the sufferer impressed with the necessity of securing a daily action, whether any inclination be felt or not.' From 'Medical and Commercial Recipes' by J.T.Butterworth published in Leeds, 1897.

Keeping regular was seen as the cornerstone of good health. Vast amounts of patent aperients were inflicted on long suffering families by loving parents. The weekly dose was vital and self-help books and the great and the good constantly denounced the evils of constipation. A Victorian journal thundered, 'women are especially addicted to the injurious habit of neglecting to solicit a periodical evacuation of the bowels.'

★ ★ ★ ★ ★

My mother did not allow constipation so every Friday night we had a dose of syrup of figs or Beechams Pills.

Henry T. Charlton, Hull

In my childhood we always had on top of our Yorkshire range three brown earthenware stewpots. The first contained scalded lemons with Epsom salts to clear the blood, in another senna pods – a gentle laxative, and the other contained stewed pearl barley and the liquid from this was for drinking to clear your waterworks. The seeds were saved and given to us as a pudding with a sprinkle of sugar. Every Sunday morning we were given a spoonful of treacle mixed with sulphur to stop us having spots.

Jean Booth, Sheffield

For constipation my mother used to give me Spanish liquorice from our local herbalist in warm water. It did the trick.

R. Bray, Cleckheaton

I found this in an old handwritten cookery book. The writer had noted that Miss Penelope was 8 years old on 11th March 1931. The remedy is called 'Miss Penelope's Medicine' and you must take a quarter of a pound each of prunes and figs and soak overnight in 1 pint of water. Then stew together with half a pound of Golden Syrup. Put all through a sieve and add 1 ounce of powdered senna and a pinch of ginger. Poor Penelope!

J. Addison, Northallerton

A collection in the Thackray Medical Museum. Essential items in every home – patent medicines. Syrup of figs for the bowels and ipecacuanha, an expectorant for coughs. (Ann Holubecki, by kind permission of the Thackray Medical Museum, Leeds)

In the bleak midwinter ... The two-holer bucket privy round the back of the barn, well away from the house. The river when it flooded provided an easy method of disposal. In conditions like these is it any wonder constipation was a problem?

Eat plenty of fruit and vegetables, take senna tea with lemon or Epsom Salts; if obstinate inject very soapy water. From *A Book for Every Home.*
Colin Chippindale, Great Horton

For constipation, and this was awful, it was a pellet made of soap and pushed up the back passage.
Sheila McFarlane, Hebden Bridge

Along with friends of less ancient vintage, I remember being made to sit for ages on a chamber pot filled with hot water supposedly to cure constipation. I cannot remember it helping.
Edna Simpson, Bradford

To keep the system clear mix Gregory Powder with a little water and take a teaspoon weekly. To make Gregory Powder mix half an ounce each of magnesia, ground ginger and Turkey rhubarb.
Jean Stinson, Northallerton

Inside a two-holer privy that has seen much action, with the possible cause – an old bottle of syrup of figs manufactured by Bleasdale Ltd of York.

'I may be some time ...!' The harsh winter of 1963 saw the privy brought back into use after the pipes froze in this house in Wensleydale. Younger members of the family were appalled and risked constipation, Sanna Middleton was made of stronger stuff. (Marjorie Middleton)

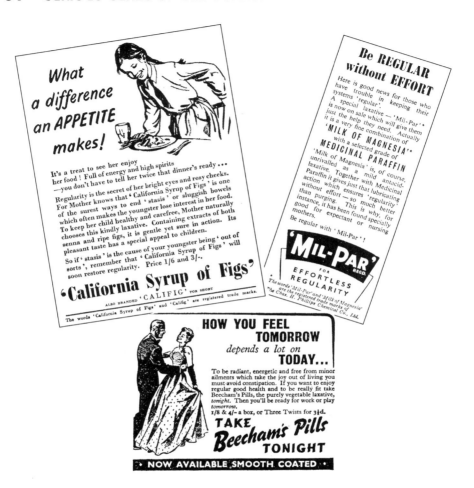

Even in the 1950s advertisements stressing the importance of keeping regular were in every magazine and newspaper.

A red hot poker put into a cup of water made cinder tea for trapped wind, and stewed rhubarb bottled with castor oil for constipation.

Jean Booth, Sheffield

Liquid paraffin for opening the bowels.

Grace Handley, Settle

An old remedy to cure diarrhoea. Sit over a chamber pot containing chamomile flowers boiled in milk.

Thackray Medical Museum, Leeds

I came across my mother's recipe for diarrhoea which is very old. Mix a quarter of an ounce each of Turkey rhubarb, capsicum, camphor, laudanum and peppermint. Take 12 to 14 drops in a little sweetened water.

E. Oliver, Burstwick

★ ★ ★ ★ ★

My mother came from Hessle. She was hardworking with eight children and did the washing for 13 other families. Her remedy for an upset stomach was to beat the white of an egg and put in half a pint of cold tap water and drink. She swore by it and I have given it to my children.

Vera Worsnop, Withernsea

From grandmother's cookbook a remedy for heartburn and indigestion. 1 dram of bismuth, 2 teaspoons of bicarbonate of soda, 20 drops of peppermint essence. Put in medicine bottle and fill up with water.

Ronda Ashworth, Heptonstall

From my grandfather Edward Brown of Bainbridge's recipe book dated 1895, a remedy given to him by a Mr Woodmass who got it from a London Specialist. 'For an ulcerated stomach, this has been found to cure many a one without an operation. Also for indigestion and flatulence. Mix together 1 ounce of bismuth, half an ounce each of soda and citrate of magnesia and take a flat teaspoonful in a little milk. Olive oil was the main cure for the ulcer along with this.'

He also had a remedy from 'old Mrs Parrington of Bentham' for anyone troubled with their water. Make tea of Robin Run-in-hedge which he identified as 'that small

Dr Jenner's for Indigestion, celebrating the Festival of Britain in 1951.

sticky stuff' but is in fact ground ivy. It will do either fresh picked or hung up in bunches and dried. Then use as liked.

Rita Cloughton, Bainbridge

For travel sickness sit on brown paper and for seasickness stuff a wad of brown paper underneath your foundation garment. Told to me by my aunt when I was going across to Norway by boat 30 years ago – it worked.

Thelma Howden, Middleham

★ ★ ★ ★ ★

Constipation is often a result of lack of roughage and fluids. Apart from diet our forebears were not helped having a cold and inhospitable outside bucket privy at the bottom of the garden or across the yard. This was not conducive to lingering and would have meant many a rushed movement. Turkey rhubarb was a 'cure all' and used the root of the plant. Gregory Powder was made up by chemists and there was even a Gregory Dinner Pill which you ate after dinner, rather as we would have the After Eight Mints. Medical thinking frowns now on the constant use of laxatives and attention to diet is urged. However, Miss Penelope's prunes would have been helpful.

Eating too much rich or fatty food or heavy drinking can give rise to painful indigestion. Bicarbonate of soda or an antacid brings relief and this seems to have been fully understood judging from these remedies. Bismuth helps in painful conditions of the bowels and stomach and has a sedative action. Capsicum, otherwise known as the pepper, was thought to relieve digestive problems. Ground ivy has been used for centuries for kidney complaints and as a diuretic. Peppermint improves digestion and can aid those suffering with flatulence. Chamomile was known for its calming effects on the digestive system and olive oil has long been known on the Continent as a cure for flatulence. Anyone foolish enough to holiday outside Yorkshire in foreign, warmer climes will know that it doesn't work!

THE RITES OF SPRING

'Tender handed stroke a nettle, and it stings you for your pains; Grasp it like a man of mettle, and it soft as silk remains.' 18th century proverb.

Springtime saw increased activity in the bowel department. It was the time for clearing out and pepping up a system made sluggish over the winter months. Drinking nettle water plus extra brimstone and treacle cleared the skin, and much else beside. In countless kitchens the spring pudding was cooked. The main ingredient was bistort, known in country areas as Passion Dock or Easterman Giant, a corruption of Easter-mangient, meaning a plant to be eaten at that time. This pudding was variously known as Easter-Ledge pudding, Herb pudding or Nettle and Passion Dock pudding.

Bistort, otherwise known as Easter-Ledge, Passion Dock or Easterman Giant grows in meadows and grassy roadsides. Here it has been cultivated in Pat and Colin Jackson's garden in Carperby. The luxurious leaves were the essential ingredient of Easter-Ledge pudding.

The helpful dockleaf always to be found near stinging nettles. It was often grown near an outside privy and used instead of lavatory paper. (Ann Holubecki)

For a good cleanser of the system around Eastertime pick young nettle tops and young Passion Dock leaves and wash them. Cut up and fry in butter and add a handful of oatmeal. At this stage it looks just like a cowpat! You can put in a couple of eggs while it is cooking on the stove. We used to eat it with fried bacon as a main course in springtime and it was lovely.

Lyn Cooper, Wyke

We always used the spring growth or new growth where the nettles had been previously cut. When I was young we would go collecting the nettles and make nettle beer, a good healthy drink, which we would all drink for pleasure. Pick 2 lbs of young nettle tops, rinse, drain and boil in water for 15 minutes. Strain into a bowl and add the peel of 2 lemons (but not the white pith), the lemon juice, 1 lb demerara sugar and 1 ounce cream of tartar. Stir well and when cool add some yeast. Keep covered with a cloth in a warm room for 3 days then strain and bottle. Keep a week before drinking. I have served nettles and they are just like spinach when cooked with a little water and served with butter, salt and pepper. A friend once wrote, 'Everytime I see a nettle I think of you!'

Edna Simpson, Bradford

What goodness we overlook growing freely in our hedgerows. Bistort contains tannin, useful as a medical astringent but the glorious nettle has the lot: highly nutritious with vitamins A and C, iron, formic acid, ammonia, silicic acid and histamine. Nettles help in the relief of rheumatism, anaemia, improve circulation, purify the system and have a general toning effect on the body. Guaranteed to put a spring in the step of most people.

A RASH OF BOILS AND OTHER ERUPTIONS

'Travellers and others have much risk to run in having unclean sheets supplied to sleep in, the consequence is some skin disease, such as the itch, tantamount to ringworm, for which sulphur baths should be used immediately.' Katy Nolan's book of 'Valuable Home Recipes'.

You do not hear much about boils these days. In past years most people suffered, especially young men round the back of the neck. Was this due to the excessive starching of collars? Perhaps shirts were not changed on a daily basis and given the hard work associated with washday, who can blame them. Bacteria could have a field day inside a dirty, sweaty collar rubbing the germs into the hair follicles.

Gone too is the telltale sign of gentian violet on a shaved head, which could only mean one thing – the highly infectious impetigo.

Many people spoke of being dosed to clear a springtime rash and the complexion. Perhaps with the better weather people went outdoors more and suffered insect bites, although there is a spring allergy called vernal conjunctivitis. Certainly skins become sallow and unhealthy during the winter and those prone to spots can suffer an outbreak on a skin starved of sunlight.

Before vaccination measles was a serious illness and in undernourished and delicate children could lead to complications. As well as a rash, eyes could become sore and red, and anxious mothers confined the child to a darkened room.

★ ★ ★ ★ ★

BOILS

In my childhood in the 1930s for a boil on the back of the neck you found a fresh cowpat, put it in some gauze and placed on the boil to 'draw' it.

Another method for boils was to put a cup full of boiling water into a milk bottle, empty the water out and place the hot milk bottle over the boil and leave it in place. As it cools it draws the pus out of the boil. The

Many people made their own preparation of Zam-Buk. According to Mattie Furnish of Castle Bolton, who has an old family recipe, the main ingredients were eucalyptus oil, swallow oil (from the celandine and often used as an embrocation) and vaseline. This advertisement dates from 1909.

suction and the pain was so intense that my friend's mother had to get a hammer to break the milk bottle.

Mac Webster, Sheffield

For drawing boils mother used poppy heads and sometimes chamomile flowers made into a poultice. She bought her herbs from James Robinson and Sons of Bradford who boasted they had the largest stock of herbs in Yorkshire. They published their own book dedicated to all those 'who would live a healthy, happy and useful life.'

Edna Simpson, Bradford

For boils drink your own urine.

Anon, Keighley

Once I had a boil in a very awkward place on my bum and my mother made me sit upstairs at night time on a potty containing water, as hot as I could bear, mixed with Epsom Salts.

Anon, Bishopdale

I got this remedy from an old gentleman in Kettlewell. For a boil, cook a jacket potato in the oven. Then put cooked potato into a silk stocking and place onto boil or abscess.

Harold Hammond, Askrigg

My father-in-law from Hull told me that a soap and sugar poultice is good for boils and also a bread poultice made from bread boiled in some water and wrapped in a clean bandage.

Wendy Milner, Gargrave

As a boy in Leeds my mother would drop 2 inch squares of lint in a pan of boiling water. Lifting them out on the end of a spoon and using a towel for protection, she wrung them out until they were almost dry but still very hot. These were placed on the boil on the back of my neck and held there with a pad of cotton wool to keep the heat in. She did this about ten times every morning and evening to draw the pus out. She called this treatment 'hot fomentation'. It was very painful.

Ray Lewis, Carperby

From mother's handwritten book a cure for boils. 1 lb of figs, 4 ounces of figwort, boil together with 2 quarts of water for 30 minutes. Get 1 ounce of saltpetre. Take a wineglass three times a day, adding as much saltpetre each time as will go on a threepenny bit.

Nora Shuttleworth, Birkenshaw

As a child I suffered from boils on my knees and elbows. Instead of being taken to the doctor's surgery my grandmother offered her remedy. My mother was instructed to beat three raw eggs and apply the mixture to some muslin. This was then applied to the boils and a bandage of brown parcel paper was placed around the muslin. This poultice was to be kept on overnight and I was assured the boils would have miraculously vanished the following day. It was a very unpleasant sensation keeping the concoction on overnight. The next day I awoke and excitedly removed the brown paper and muslin. To my horror, not only were the boils still there, as red and as sore as ever, but the eggs had scrambled! Not a cure I would recommend.

Deborah Ransome, Sprotbrough

My Dad once had a carbuncle (a collection of boils) under his arm. My Mum put him a linseed poultice on and when she came to take it off it was stuck to him. He told her to pull it, which she did, but of course it was stuck to the hairs as well. He gave a scream of agony and the next thing she was in the next door neighbour's house. He was a quiet man but there was no knowing what he would have done that day if she had not fled!

Edna Markham, Crookes

About 1912 my father, a farmer at Bainbridge, was laid low with boils on his neck. The doctors could do nothing so he went to Bradford to see a specialist whose cure sounds like a witch doctor's. Take a shotgun cartridge, pour out and discard the lead shot and wadding but pour the black gunpowder onto a sheet of paper. Each evening take a glass of warm water and place as much gunpowder as will lay on a sixpence and mix this amount into the water stirring well. Drink this mixture on rising next morning. He was cured in a few days!

Anon, Swaledale

RASHES AND SPOTS

We drank large quantities of nettle water in the Spring as it was considered good for the complexion and cleaning the blood. But through the year we drank hot cabbage water for the complexion and getting rid of spots.

May Robinson, Skeeby Women's Institute

In the Spring we had brimstone and treacle to prevent spotty faces. Mother made her own with 1 lb of treacle and ½ lb of sulphur well mixed. We were given a dessert-spoonful every week.

Henry T. Charlton, Hull

John Wesley believed that eating marigold flowers as a sallad (sic) with oil and vinegar prevented the plague and that the juice from the marigold cured it. The nursery rhyme 'Ring-a-ring o'roses' describes the symptoms of the plague but the second, less well-known, verse might be describing this cure, 'Down in the meadow eating buttercups, Atishoo, atishoo, we all stand up.'

For nettle rash rub on dock leaves, but chew them to make them soft and this soothes the rash.

Grace Handley, Settle

From my grandmother Alice Johnson's herb notes. For spots on the arms and shoulders rub the juice of a raw greengage into them and repeat twice a day for two days without washing off. Then bathe in hot water with wild flower petals in it.

Fox Johnson, Saltaire

For acne or blackheads press out with a watch key and apply sulphur ointment. Taken from *A Book for Every Home.*

Colin Chippindale, Great Horton

From the Swillington Methodist Ladies Bright Hour: For itchy skin wash the parts affected with strong rum. Steep a shirt for 30 minutes in a quart of water mixed with 1 ounce of powdered brimstone. Dry it slowly and wear for 5 to 6 days. Frequently take a warm bath, the greatest cures have been effected by it.

Barbara Evans, Swillington

A couple of tablespoons of bicarbonate of soda in the bath water takes the burning out and stops the itching of chicken pox.

Mac Webster, Sheffield

Paste for insect bites. Into a small jar put 1 tablespoon of glycerine, 2 tablespoons of honey and stand the jar in hot water and stir until well blended. Add 2 teaspoons of boracic acid powder and stir until cold.

Margaret May, Almondbury

MEASLES

An old remedy for measles was the plant called cleavers (also known as goosegrass or Sticky Willie) made into a drink to draw out the poisons of infection.

Thackray Medical Museum, Leeds

For measles we used to take the paper from the blue sugar bags and place onto the bedroom light bulb to darken the room. You must not open the curtain.

Grace Handley, Settle

My father's remedy for 'gowly' (Yorkshire for 'stuck together') eyes was to stew young ivy leaves. The eyes were bathed in a weak, warm solution of this and it was soothing, especially for anyone with measles. Nowadays we are warned in herbalist textbooks that all parts of the ivy are poisonous and on no account must be eaten.

Jean Booth, Sheffield

WHITLOW

For a whitlow under the finger nail make a hot poultice of bread and boiling water. I remember Grandma applying this to my finger, I screamed – pulled away the finger and she was left clutching the hot poultice.

Sheila McFarlane, Hebden Bridge

ULCERS

For leg ulcers boil a couple of handfuls of bran. Strain off the liquid and let it cool. Bathe the ulcerated leg in the liquid using a sponge. Dry and put a bandage on. It has a healing effect. The old lady who brought me up had leg ulcers and she didn't bother the doctor with them.

Lyn Cooper, Wyke

An old farmer told me that for ulcerated legs get some dock-leaves, shred them in some water and bring them to the boil. Simmer for an hour. Apply the liquid to the legs.

Mac Webster, Sheffield

STYES

If you feel a stye coming on use your own spit to rub on it but it must be the first spit of the day.

Ros Collin, Skeeby Women's Institute

When I was a lad of 13 I had a stye on my eye. An old lady I knew told me to get a rotten apple and fold a handkerchief. Spread the rotten apple on the first fold and tie it round your head and sleep with it on your stye. When I woke up in the morning the stye had gone and I have never had another.

D. Vaughan, Bradford

For a stye my mother rubbed it with her wedding ring.

May Robinson, Skeeby Women's Institute

Quite frequently I suffered what mother called 'blast' in my eyes. It felt as though there was something in them. We collected figwort every year and it was dried and then scalded, cooled and enclosed in a linen bag to apply to my eyes.

Edna Simpson, Allerton

A stye on the eye was cured by bathing it in warm water or boracic powder.

Sheila McFarlane, Hebden Bridge

Our family called styes 'blains' and cold tea bags placed on the stye and kept on with a bandage overnight brings them to a head.

*Sharon Capper, Northwich**

CORNS

To treat corns my father Clifford Watson used to squeeze some lemon juice into a basin and mix with Epsom Salts to make a paste. This was put onto the corn, then an old sock over the foot with the corn – so you didn't mark the sheets. Apply morning and night for a week. In addition steep your feet in Epsom Salts mixed with hot water, they are a great 'drawing' agent.

Audrey Bailey, Thoralby

Rub corns with the side of a matchbox.

June Stringfellow and Joyce Flynn, Pontefract

For a painful corn add 2 tablespoons of flour to 2 teaspoons of mustard powder. Mix to a paste with a little cold water then add 1 pint of hot water. Soak your feet in this once a week.

Nora Shuttleworth, Birkenshaw

From great-grandfather's accounts book. Rub a little oil of peppermint to ease a sore corn.

Susan Burnell, Swillington

For corns my father would crush an ivy leaf which was then put on the corn and covered with an elastoplast. Leave it for two weeks and do not get it wet. It kills the corn and the elastoplast is easy to remove.

Elaine Cockram, Huddersfield

Boils are now treated successfully with penicillin but the hot fomentation and various poultices were an effective if painful way of dealing with them. The heat dilated the blood vessels and softened the skin to help the boil come to a 'point' and burst. The milk bottle treatment must have been agonising.

Boils often occur when people are 'run down'. After a winter without many green vegetables, a dose of nettles could only do you good. Rich in vitamins A and C and minerals, especially iron, the tops of young spring nettles cooked and eaten or as a drink are a tonic. Think of the nettle and you think of its nasty sting but it has long been known to be helpful in clearing toxins and for skin complaints.

Figwort and cleavers have both been used for centuries in treating skin diseases and inflammation. Chamomile soothes irritated skin. Brimstone, another name for sulphur, was used extensively and is present in many modern external acne treatments. Saltpetre was a constituent of gunpowder and a preservative and in past times taken

Old pharmacy bottles and preparations including camphor squares, sal volatile and Reckitt's Blue Bag for an added whiteness to clothes and to soothe stings. (Ann Holubecki)

internally as a medicine; perhaps that was what the business with the shotgun cartridge was all about.

Carbolic soap has antiseptic properties and bicarbonate of soda is a weak alkali which is helpful for bee stings which are acid. Wasp stings, which are alkali, need vinegar. The alkaline secretions of a dock leaf, especially the smaller 'sour dockings' are very effective against nettle stings once mixed with saliva. However, many mothers favoured the washday 'dolly blue' cure which left curious blue stains on the skin.

Boracic acid powder, a mild antiseptic is now considered unsuitable for babies and young children. Ivy leaves were used externally for skin eruptions but are not recommended now as all parts of the ivy are poisonous.

WARTS

*In the 1920s one of the youngsters in the family put a lot of sulphur
on his warty knuckles and then ran his hand along the wall on
his way to school. The flames cured the warts!*
Catharine M. Parker, Threshfield.

There are many cures and superstitions surrounding the ugly subject of warts which range from the fairly sensible to the bizarre. Warts disfigure the face and hands and people were ashamed of them. Fairy stories have the witch with the obligatory black cat, broomstick and giant wart on the face: if you want to make a character hideous give them a wart. Warts were plentiful and part of childhood but there was always someone in the neighbourhood who could furnish a cure.

★ ★ ★ ★ ★

I had one remedy which was successful in my young days. At 8 years old I had a lot of warts on the back of my hands. My father made me rub them at bedtime with warm castor oil and I am now 78 and have never been troubled since.

Leonard Western, Sheffield

Rub the wart with a cut raw potato and bury the potato in the garden.
June Stringfellow and Joyce Flynn, Pontefract

Put a piece of raw beef on top of the wart. Wish it to go away, then hide the piece of beef and do not tell a soul where you have hidden it. The wart will go away eventually – mine did in 1947.

R. Bray, Cleckheaton

My friend Peter Oberon is the blacksmith at Preston Park Museum near Yarm. Under the smithy fire is a container called the 'bosh' holding the water to cool your tools. This dirty water is called 'bosh water'. Put some of this water in a jam jar and last thing at night dab some on your wart and let it dry. We knew a gentleman with terrible warts under his chin, so bad he could not shave, he dabbed this 'bosh water' on and within 8 days was cured. I have also known this to cure warts on children when nothing from the chemist or doctor would do the trick.

Richard Skeene, Tunstall

An old lady I knew told me that if you ever get a wart, wet a match and dab the brimstone on the wart and in a week it will go.

D. Vaughan, Bradford

From my childhood in Leeds I remember being told to use the striking side of a used matchbox and sandpaper the wart away.

Ray Lewis, Carperby

I was told to wrap a piece of cardboard around the wart and keep it on and within the week it had gone.

Barbara Evans, Swillington

I always treated any warts with the milk from a dandelion stem. The milk dried dark brown and it seemed to work. Another benefit of this treatment was that it reduced the dandelions in the garden so they never got a chance to flower.

Denny Minnitt, Askrigg

When we were children everything was horse-drawn. Dad would go out and pull out a hair from the horse's tail, the horse did not seem to notice. You tied the horse hair round the wart and after a while it would drop off.

Edna Markham, Crookes

I heard tell that you must rub a wart with a black snail then put the snail on a thorn on a thorn bush. As the snail dies the wart will go away, but you must not let anyone see you do it.

Mary Bostock, Castle Bolton

Steal a piece of lean meat before noon, rub the wart with it and bury it in the garden. Tell no one or the cure is useless. As the flesh rots the wart will wither away.

Yorkshire folk lore

From a book on witchcraft published in Bedale in 1773. Frog spit rubbed on a wart or rubbed on a pig's back, or wash your hands with water in which eggs have been boiled are certain cures.

Den Chisholm, Marton

Rub warts daily with any one of the following: a radish, juice of a dandelion or marigold flowers, fish liver, mole's blood or swine's blood, fasting spittle, elder leaves or flowers and finally eat largely of watercress.

From John Wesley's 'Primitive Physic'

There are different kinds of warts and the problem in getting rid of them is that they are viruses and slightly contagious. You are therefore dealing with something quite tricky which is likely to disappear on its own or remain with you for years.

Are these cures all the result of mind over matter? It is acknowledged that 'suggestion therapy' is successful and if you tell the 'warty one' with authority that you can cure the affliction, you are half way there. Odd rituals add to the mystique but spearing live snails would be frowned on in these more enlightened times.

Anything with an abrasive quality might be useful in reducing the wart. The dandelion has some powerful properties and the juice from the stalk could probably tackle a wart. My mother, who was a southerner, claimed the opposite of the witchcraft cure, water in which eggs had been hardboiled caused warts.

Several people knew of the benefits to be had from human saliva, especially first thing in the morning before breakfast. The first spit of the day or 'fastin' spittle dabbed onto warts or a stye on the eye was a common cure. Saliva has a natural chemical called lysozyme which heals cuts. The saliva gland produces powerful digestive enzymes so perhaps it is not so far fetched to consider that saliva could banish a wart. As for frog spit – how would you obtain it?

KIDDING PILLS

'During the 1940s doctors would prescribe what they called "kidding" pills. These were either brown or white and sugar coated.'
Mac Webster, Sheffield.

I was born in 1931 and during the Second World War as a young boy I helped out Mr Bellamy the local chemist in the little mining and farming village of Beighton. We had two extra weeks off school to help with the potato crop but I helped Mr Bellamy in the chemist shop. I was about twelve at the time and he called me from the dispensary and said, 'You can come and count these.' I replied, 'But I'm not supposed to touch the drugs.' Mr Bellamy replied, 'Ah, it's alright these are "kidding" pills.'

There were two types of pills prescribed by Dr Dedombal, who would tell the patient that it was a new type of drug and give them the white ones first. If they did not get better they were to go back to see him and he would prescribe something stronger – the brown pill.

These were hard, stressful times. People worked long hours in the mines and munition factories and after a day's work they would have a couple of hours at home and then go and work on the land. The 'kidding' pills were not a cruel deception, it was all the medical profession had to help and at least

Advice from the leather-bound 'commonplace' book of Mr Edward Brown of Bainbridge dated 1895. Cures for humans in the front and even more cures for animals in the back. These included 'for cows not holding the bull' a mixture of vinegar and crushed soda, and 'tremble in sheep' a pleasant mixture of warm beer, yeast and treacle.

people felt they were being attended to; often that alone makes you feel better.

Mac Webster, Sheffield

My mother before marriage was General Help to Dr Grime, a Hawes doctor. She had to make up the various red and white mixtures. It was all the same – bicarbonate of soda – but the white had peppermint in and the red had cochineal plus various flavours.

Anon, Swaledale

Around the 1890s in Bainbridge, Wensleydale there were several little shops in one of which was the apothecary, who died suddenly. George, who owned the property, had to clear the apothecary's shop out quickly. There were pills of all sorts, sizes and colours and soon Tommy, the village hypochondriac, was around to see what was going free.

George showed him all the pills and said he could have them. He recommended that Tommy took a white one and a blue one each day and a big red one with the others on a Sunday and this would keep him healthy.

After about ten days George met Tommy and asked how he was. He replied, 'Oh fine – but I've only had my braces on one button for the last week, I've been to the privy that many times!'

PAIN IN THE NECK

'Do not visit the sick when you are fatigued, or when in a state of perspiration, or with the stomach empty – for in such conditions you are liable to take the infection.' The Wensleydale and Swaledale Almanack, 1909.

Tonsillitis is a common illness in children with the tonsils and the back of the throat inflamed, often with white flecks of pus. A complication can lead to quinsy, an abscess under the mucous membrane surrounding the tonsils making it difficult to swallow, speak and open the mouth. An altogether miserable illness. Tonsils are important in protecting the body against infection. At one time doctors whipped tonsils out at the drop of a hat but now seem less inclined. It was such a common experience up until the late 1930s that often the operation, where the tonsils were 'guillotined', took place on the kitchen table! One assumes the tea things were cleared first.

★ ★ ★ ★ ★

From the Swillington Methodist Ladies Bright Hour: for a sore throat, drink a teaspoonful of warm vinegar very slowly.

I remember having a hot, boiled onion cut in half and put in a sweaty sock and tied round my neck. I had to sleep with it on and many a time it was better in the morning.

Barbara Evans, Swillington

My father's remedy for a sore throat was a teaspoon of sugar, add some vinegar until it was well soaked in and take when required. It definitely works!

D. Chapman, Hornsea

Warm a pat of butter, a teaspoon of sugar and 1 tablespoon of vinegar. Sip when needed.

E. Ellis, Sheffield

Granny Myatt's cure for a sore throat. Take a sheet of clean notepaper. Fold in two and carefully put a spoonful of flowers of sulphur in the middle of the fold. Sit patient facing window, open their mouth, then blow in sulphur. I can still remember the pandemonium when Granny

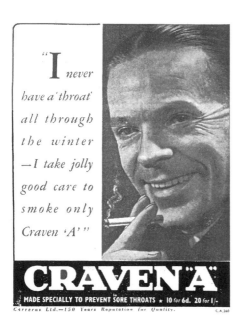

"I never have a 'throat' all through the winter —I take jolly good care to smoke only Craven 'A'"

CRAVEN "A"

MADE SPECIALLY TO PREVENT SORE THROATS ★ 10 for 6d. 20 for 1/-

Carreras Ltd.—150 Years Reputation for Quality.   C.A.260

This advertisement of 1936 for Craven 'A' made the extraordinary claim, in the light of what we know now, to prevent sore throats. Thousands will have believed it.

was about to administer this remedy to my uncle, then 18 – he blew first!

Hilda Jackson, Bedale

My mother-in-law was born in Driffield in 1893 and in her recipe book are several cures. For a sore throat fill a medicine bottle half full of cold tea. In this dissolve 1 teaspoon of salt, then add 1 tablespoon of vinegar. Put a tablespoon of the mixture into half a cup of warm water and gargle every 4 hours.

G. Rawling, Keighley

My grandmother's remedy for a sore throat was to put a piece of fat bacon around the neck at bedtime. This was held in place with the left leg of a stocking. The next morning the bacon was almost cooked but what had been a sore throat the night before was very much better. I never found out, or even wondered why it had to be the left leg stocking.

*Ken Tyers, Consett, Co Durham**

Grandmother lived in Sheffield and during the war she brought us up as mother had to work. She had a copy of *Every Housewife's Guide Book*, a collection of 'reliable confectionery, medical and miscellaneous recipes.' A liniment for sore throats or quinsy – mix together 1 ounce each of turpentine, liquid ammonia and olive oil. Apply with a flannel to the throat.

Brenda Marsh, Sheffield

My mother looked after lots of 'theatricals' staying at the Grand Hotel, Scarborough for the summer season. From her 'commonplace' book comes the advice to chew a small piece of tangerine peel to soothe a sore throat.

Eileen Crabtree, Ramsgill

Gargle with whisky and then swallow it.

Audrey Bailey, Thoralby

Great-grandfather William Elston from Leeds cured hoarseness by baking a lemon, as you would an apple. Squeeze a little of the thickened and hot juice over a lump of sugar and take frequently.

Susan Burnell, Swillington

From *A Book for Every Home*: 5 parts elderberry syrup mixed to 1 part honey is soothing for sore throats. For hoarseness hot milk boiled with a little suet.

Colin Chippindale, Great Horton

For laryngitis mix together 1 tablespoon each of honey, glycerine, lemon juice or vinegar and take a spoonful as required. I know this works when antibiotics do not always.

Lyn Cooper, Wyke

Black burnt toast soaked in vinegar, warmed, put in a stocking and tied round your throat.

Mary Bostock, Castle Bolton

For quinsy, hot salt in a stocking tied under the chin.

M. Brandon, Mytholmroyd

Raspberry vinegar and olive oil are good for a sore throat.

Catharine M. Parker, Threshfield

For a sore throat Grandma, who lived in Huddersfield, would boil potatoes, mash them and wrap them in a little cloth. The cloth was put into one of her stockings and then olive or camphorated oil rubbed onto the outside of the stocking. Then wrap the stocking round the neck until morning. It was a soggy lump in the morning but the sore throat had gone.

Mrs Addy, Bradley

Tonsillitis is a miserable illness and even now there is not a lot to be done apart from drinking plenty and going to bed until the worst is over. Antibiotics are prescribed if the cause is bacterial, but have no effect on a virus. Flowers of sulphur has disinfectant properties but is no longer obtainable as it is an ingredient in the making of explosives. The astringency of lemon juice, vinegar, raspberry vinegar and salt would help reduce swollen and inflamed tissue. Olive oil, honey, sugar and syrup would certainly soothe. In adults the comfort of something warm in a stocking wrapped round the throat might make you feel better, but then again if you are feeling very ill, the solitary bliss of the spare bedroom might seem attractive.

THE CURES

I n the days before we had national health, there was doctor's cards
but little wealth.
The medicines were all home made, for the doctor's bills you had to
save.
You had to wait for an operation, when enough was saved there was
great jubilation.

Now Minnie and I had both been bad, with septic tonsils two weeks we'd
had.
The doctor was called and said to our Mam, 'They'll have to come out as
quick as you can.'
Now only one could have this pleasure, he decided Minnie's could be left
for a longer leisure.
Whether it was the smile that dazzled him, but he put her name down
instead of mine.
From hospital she came after only one day, so weak and pale did she lay.
Then Mam gave her jelly and ice cream to eat, and to us kids this was a
great treat.

But our Pam was always the sickly one, she caught everything going
under the sun.
Our Mam must have been driven to hysteria, for if it had been hanging
around, she'd have caught malaria.
She always had styes and boils and such, with whitlows on her fingers
she dare not touch.
With ears running she would not tell Mam, for something concocted
would come out of the pan.
Now Mam said, 'Mrs Smith has give me this tip', she said 'it was sure to do
the trick.'
An onion she'd picked and cooked in the skin, when she took the middle
out it was very thin.
Then she placed it boiling inside of Pat's ear, our Pat screamed out and
looked very queer.

Then there was senna pods to go to the loo, and cold cabbage water was
   very good too.
A teaspoon of sulphur to clean out the blood, if she added treacle it
   tasted quite good.
Sugar and soap to draw out an abscess, but a kaolin poultice was a
   quicker success.
The fat bacon rind drew out boils too and lots more cures she had to do.
When we had mumps this was another thing, sweaty socks with roast
   tattie, tied around you with string.

Sometimes the cure was worse than the complaint, and God help us all if
   we said we felt faint!
When we look back now we sometimes wonder, how we reached this
   age despite all this blunder.
But I'm glad our Mam never sought advice from farmer, for now we are
   all much older and wiser;
If he'd told her then of a certain cure, we'd have been covered in his best
   manure!

Anne Telfer, Hartlepool

PAINS, SPRAINS AND CHILBLAINS

'Rheumatism is greatly relieved by wearing a wash leather over the afflicted part.' Katy Nolan's book of 'Valuable Home Recipes'.

Rheumatics used to cover just about every ache and pain that hard manual toil inflicted on the body. Heavy, relentless work in engineering, mining and farming carried out in harsh conditions all took a toll on the body. The resulting pain and stiffness was often called 'rheumatism' and relief sought from the contents of the 'rubbing bottle'.

Colin Gorman of Coxhoe in County Durham treasures a piece of paper written in copperplate handwriting 'Receit for the Rheumatism – John Dinsdale – Marrick December 13th 1848.' His great-great-grandfather's life was that of an ordinary, decent man living and working against the odds. The physical hardships visited on John Dinsdale were typical and his life an example of the vicissitudes of ordinary people. Born in Marrick in Swaledale in 1800, he married Mary and a son was born. Mary died and he married Ann who bore him a further four sons. He was knowledgeable about herbs and a man of some learning but he kept his family by farming and as a lead miner, working both jobs together. Lead miners travelled long distances to work on foot, often knitting as they

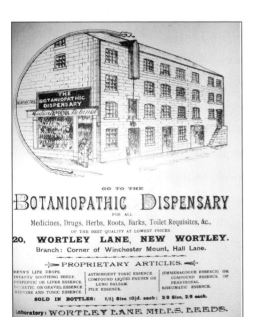

Medical Botany, popular in the north in the 1800s, believed that disease was caused by cold in the body. Plant drugs and cayenne pepper were used to produce internal heat. (Ann Holubecki, by kind permission of the Thackray Medical Museum, Leeds)

walked. Imagine the walk through the hills in appalling weather, a day's work, the walk home and then some farming. No wonder John's body ached. When the lead mines closed John, Ann and the five sons moved to County Durham to work in the coal-mines. He died in 1872 at the age of 76, a life unremarked but yet courageous.

For rubbing liniment take 2 ounces each of turpentine, spirit of hartshorn (an old word for sal volatile), linseed oil and olive oil. Bottle and shake well.

Margaret May, Almondbury

Arnica, opodeldoc (soap liniment) and olive oil. An old remedy for arthritic joints but a very elderly friend still used this into the 1990s and it worked.

Warmed rock salt wrapped in a flannel and placed on the painful area.

Catharine M. Parker, Threshfield

For rheumatism mix 1 gill of white wine vinegar, 1 ounce crushed saltpetre and half an ounce of cayenne pepper. Put all the ingredients

Ann Holubecki mixing a cupful of vinegar and turpentine, a piece of camphor and an egg to make an old-fashioned rubbing liniment, watched by Tyne Tees presenter Heather McWilliam and cameraman Steve Falvey.

together into a bottle and shake well. Apply the affected parts with a sponge. Advice from *An Old Corner Cupboard*.

June Ford, Brighouse

I always carry a nutmeg to keep rheumatism at bay.

Anon, Wensleydale

I inherited this recipe for embrocation from my mother who was born in 1900, who in turn got it from her mother. Beat a raw new laid egg, mix with a tumbler of vinegar – add a little at a time. Add 1 teaspoon of turpentine and 30 drops of camphor spirits. Put in bottle and shake well.

Jean Laskey, Hackenthorpe

We used to live on a farm on the outskirts of Sheffield. My mother had a few remedies written at the back of her cookery book: Strengthening mixture, Peppermint, Cough Mixture and Rubbing Oil. With these four remedies she had most illnesses covered. For Rubbing Oil take 2 eggcups each of turpentine, ammonia and vinegar and mix with a 2 penny tin of mustard.

J. Hague, Oughtibridge

For a rheumatic knee put a vinegar bandage round the knee.

Mary Bostock, Castle Bolton

From the Spensley family papers of Wensleydale a cure for rheumatism: 3 ounces of spirits of turpentine, 1 ounce origanum oil and 1 dram of chloroform, mix and rub on frequently.

Christine Amsden, Redmire

Great-grandfather's cure for rheumatism. Boil either parsley or celery and drink plenty of the water or eat plenty of the outside of the celery, namely that which is normally thrown away.

Susan Burnell, Swillington

From the book of my grandfather Edward Brown of Bainbridge dated 1895. For backache mix a quarter of an ounce each of oil of juniper and spirit of lavender and half an ounce each of spirit of nitre and sal volatile: 20 drops to be taken in half a wine glass of water three times a day.

Rita Cloughton, Bainbridge

While cooking cabbage hold the arthritic joint over steam. Take great care: too difficult to do for a hip! Or make a poultice of cabbage leaves.

Anon, Wensleydale

I heard this from an old lady who had it from her grandmother. Put a cork under the pillow to stop night cramps.

Wendy Milner, Gargrave

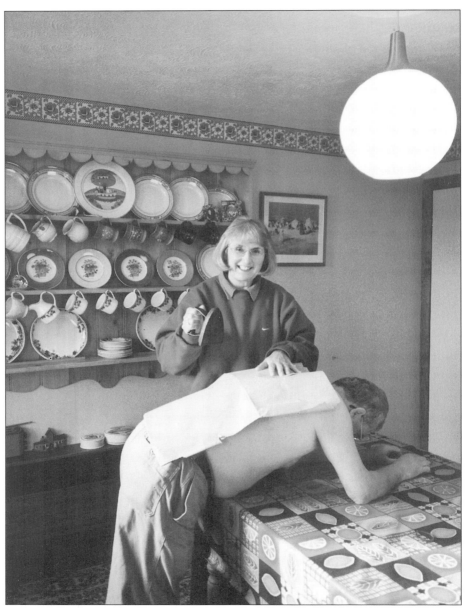

Now what's going on here?! The author is applying an old flat iron and brown paper to the back of her long-suffering husband. People who worked out in the cold all day would often have this done when they got home. It warmed the back and eased the aches.

We lived at Scapegoat Hill near Huddersfield and father once suffered with lumbago. He always carried a potato – it was always the same potato which became very shrivelled. He never suffered lumbago again.

Elaine Cockram, Huddersfield

For a bad back the miners wore a layer of Thermogene underneath a piece of blanket.

Mac Webster, Sheffield

In 1890 my grandmother Lucy Elizabeth Hill, aged 17, came to Hebden Bridge to be 'in service'. She married my grandfather Thomas Greenwood when quite young and had seven children. My mother is the youngest and she passed grandmother's cookbook on to me. There are a number of cures for rheumatism for she suffered badly with rheumatoid arthritis.

A simple remedy for rheumatism was to boil 2 lemons in a quart of water down to a pint, add 2 ounces of Epsom salts and a large spoonful of ginger. Drink a wineglass of this daily.

Ronda Ashworth, Heptonstall

I remember as a small boy being taken by my grandmother for a walk down to the river Ure. She made me collect all the sheep wool that was lying about and there and then she would pull up her skirt and push the wool down her stocking top. She claimed this helped with her rheumatism.

Michael Weatherald, Askrigg

SPRAINS

My grandma was Yorkshire born and bred and if we had a sprained wrist she would tell us to tie a strand of pure knitting wool round it and this would take the pain away and strengthen it.

Carol Mitchell, Bolton-on-Dearne

Pick fresh comfrey leaves and press very firmly into a screwtop jar. In about two weeks it will be 'ripe' and begin to turn black and then into oil. Store for about two years and do not open it to let air in. Use the oil for sprains, aches, pains and bruises.

Ann Holubecki, Redmire

My mother Emily Shaw Milner lived in Pontefract and I remember her picking comfrey at the side of the road for a sprain. She boiled the leaves for a short time then made the sodden leaves into a poultice and placed

Comfrey, otherwise known as knitbone. The leaves contain allentoin, a protein encouraging cell division. Once eaten in salads, it is now recommended that it should not be ingested. However, as a tincture or oil applied externally it is known for its healing effects. (Ann Holubecki)

BONE-SETTING in all its branches.

J. OYSTON,

BONE-SETTER,

THE GREENS,

HAWES.

Fractures, Dislocations, Stiff Joints, Sprains, &c., carefully treated.

 OILS for Sprains and Bruises.

28

From the Wensleydale and Swaledale Almanack 1918.

From the Wensleydale and Swaledale Almanack 1915. Allen's Plasters were famous throughout the Dales. The plasters were soaked in a mixture known only to Mrs Whitaker nee Allen.

them on the swelling, wrapping a bandage or old tea towel round to hold the leaves in place. This reduced the swelling. I remember going to bed with this on my leg and waking in the night with the comfrey dried out and scratching.

Valerie Lewis,
Kirkhamgate

For Rheumatic and Gout.

£2,000

And a Pension of £500 a Year for Life

was paid to the Physician who prescribed the following
remedy, by a rich patient, after a complete cure.

Guaiacum	...	1 dram
Powdered Rhubarb	...	½ ounce
Flowers Brimstone	...	2 ounces
Cream Tartar	...	1 ounce
Best Ginger	...	1½ ounces

One Nutmeg finely Powdered to be mixed well in
1-lb of Clarified Honey.

Two teaspoonfuls to be taken night and morning.

Rich rewards! From a small booklet price 5 shillings dated 1897 'Practical, Medical and Commercial Recipes' by J.T. Butterworth who had 'occupied situations in some of the best dispensary businesses of Lancashire and Yorkshire.' Guaiac is a resin from a West Indian tree.

I am a great believer in witch hazel for bruising and sprains and have had it in the house for 50 years. However, it should not be used if the skin is broken.

Sally Potter, Skeeby Women's Institute

★ ★ ★ ★ ★

CHILBLAINS

A cure for chilblains: soak your feet in the urine from the chamber pot. As a child I did this. I am now turned 80 and sometimes my feet burn and get hot at night but I no longer use the chamber pot, instead I 'wee' onto a piece of cotton wool and dab that onto my feet. Instant relief.

Anon, Skipton

Walk round the village barefoot in the snow.

Muriel Dinsdale, Carperby

Stand in the snow to stimulate the circulation. Then come inside and rub feet briskly with a rough towel. I used 'Snowfire', an oily paste available circa 1944.

Grace Handley, Settle

Great grandfather's cure for chilblains, rub with a piece of raw onion.

Susan Burnell, Swillington

Chilblains were cured by dipping a slice of onion in salt and rubbing on my ankles.

E Lynch, Pudsey

From *Old Fashioned Remedies* by the Swillington Methodist Ladies Bright Hour. Urine is very good for anything to do with your feet. When they are sweaty and aching or if you have got athlete's foot, blisters or bruises, soak your feet in a bowl of hot urine. Miners would come home with their feet all sweaty and 'wee' in the potty, then put their feet in it and leave them there until the urine got cold.

Barbara Evans, Swillington

A 1945 advertisement for Snowfire, a popular remedy for chilblains.

★ ★ ★ ★ ★

Osteoarthritis is a degenerative joint disease caused by wear and tear, rheumatoid arthritis is inflammatory but in years past people believed that cold and damp played a part in 'rheumatics'. Damp was seen as the great enemy and was everywhere in houses built without damp courses. Great emphasis was put on 'aired beds' and older people did not venture out until the 'streets were aired'. Any ingredient or rubbing action that replaced a nasty pain with a pleasant pain and bringing warmth would offer some relief. Now anti-inflammatory and painkiller drugs would be prescribed.

Nettle stings are said to be an antidote to the pain of rheumatism and arthritis and the Roman legionaries rolled in nettles to relieve their aches and pains. Pause for a second and imagine the scenes at Hadrian's Wall. Parsley and celery reduce inflammation and clear toxins and both have been known to herbalists as helping in arthritic and rheumatic complaints but eating them to excess is dangerous. Juniper berries reduce inflammation. Arnica is good for sprains and bruises. The origanum from the marjoram family is looked on now as having no useful properties and indeed can cause skin irritation.

Comfrey, also called 'knitbone', is a remarkable plant known for years to be beneficial for its healing properties, reducing inflammation and controlling bleeding. The leaf contains allentoin, a protein encouraging cell division, which is responsible for its healing properties. It works through the skin when applied as an oil or poultice.

The itching and inflammation of chilblains is caused by poor circulation and exposure to cold. The snow treatment would not be advised now as the cure is to keep the feet warm and dry but a swift walk round the village might pep up the circulation.

PRE PENICILLIN

The first finger contains poison, no ointment should be put on with it.
Use the third finger as it is harmless and in addition a lucky finger.
An old Yorkshire superstition.

S ir Alexander Fleming discovered by chance the anti-bacterial action of penicillin in 1929 and during the 1939-1945 Second World War its many practical uses were developed. Penicillin works against a huge range of bacteria but before this miraculous breakthrough cuts and wounds were treated in some very clever and novel ways. It must have been a brave man who first tried the dairy floor remedy below.

I was told an old farming remedy by an 'old farmer' for wounds which would not heal. Take two thick slices of bread, place on the floor of the dairy and leave until a green mould has appeared on them. Then mix into a salve and place on wound. This was normally used on animals but after the 1914-1918 First World War was successfully used on men who returned with bad wounds. An early form of penicillin.

John Bradshaw, Silsden

For a cut which would not stop bleeding, my grandmother used to go into the cellar, find a cobweb and spread it over the wound. It always worked and never became infected.

E. Lynch, Pudsey

My father never destroyed a cobweb as when placed on a heavily bleeding cut it stemmed the flow while stitching, if needed, was done. This worked on a horse with a badly gashed fetlock.

Jean Booth, Sheffield

For a badly cut finger my uncle put brown paper soaked in vinegar on my cut then tied it tight. I was cured within a week; my mother played pop with him – but it worked.

R. Bray, Cleckheaton

My grandmother from Carleton recommended binding a bad cut with cotton strips soaked in cranesbill solution but if no cranesbill, golden rod would do.

Fox Johnson, Saltaire

A 1915 advertisement for O.R. Bowe chemist and druggist of Hawes. One day an elderly Dales farmer went into the shop to buy some patent medicine. It cost 1 shilling and a halfpenny – a lot of money in the early 1900s. The farmer asked the chemist if he would knock off the halfpenny from the price. The chemist replied, 'I could knock off the shilling and still make a profit!' Is it any wonder that at those prices you tried to make your own medicines. (Michael Weatherald, Askrigg)

Slippery elm and marshmallow ointment was an old remedy for cuts which would not heal.

Catharine M. Parker, Threshfield

I went to school at East Witton, leaving in the mid 1930s to work on a farm 'living in' in the Thornton Watlass area. I cut my finger when sharpening a scythe, exposing the bone. A fuzzball (puff-ball fungus) was found and placed over the cut, then tied on with a spotted handkerchief. It healed perfectly and today one cannot tell where the cut had been.

Den Chisholm, Marton

My mother came from Bradford and all the old ladies used this cure for an open wound or cut that had turned nasty. On a cloth put some soap and sprinkle sugar on it. Place on wound and leave for 24 hours. It will also remove any glass or 'spells'. In the army the men used moss instead – it was all you had when you were miles from anywhere.

Jack Binns, Bradford

Make a paste of bicarbonate of soda and dab it on burns, scalds, and sunburn. When I was a fireman in the late 1950s and early 1960s we used to carry a stone jar with us in the fire engine with bicarbonate of soda in it. If anyone got burnt at the steelworks or in a house fire we would sprinkle the burn there and then with bicarb, wrap a bandage round and spray with water. For a wound we used to dab flowers of sulphur on it – better than an antibiotic.

Mac Webster, Sheffield

Cold tea leaves bound on a scald would take the heat out.

Wendy Milner, Gargrave

From *Old Fashioned Remedies* by the Swillington Methodist Ladies Bright Hour. For soothing minor burns if there is no broken skin, rub the affected part with a slice of raw potato.

Barbara Evans, Swillington

Great-grandfather's healing ointment. Elderflowers boiled in wax and olive oil.

Susan Burnell, Swillington

There was a patent medicine called Carron Oil we used in the 1920s for burns, made of equal parts linseed oil and lime water. My father was a milkman and one day during one of his coughing fits he passed out and fell on the fire. He had a linen mask put onto his face and Carron Oil painted onto it. His face healed and he had no scars. People stopped using it shortly afterwards because the authorities said oil was bad for burns but we had a very good experience with it.

Edna Simpson, Bradford

For any inflamed area we used Bate's Salve. It looked like sealing wax only black and you melted it with a match and then dripped it onto a piece of lint or cloth.

Mrs Nash, Allerton

My stepfather's father came from Shipley and must have been an interesting character. He was a cobbler but also on the side did some unofficial and illegal money lending. The earliest entries in his commonplace book are 1824 and are a mixture of mysterious accounts, recipes for different coloured inks, including invisible ink, and some medical notes. My stepfather took a friend home to his widowed mother in Shipley for tea once. She had never met this friend before and it turned out to be Albert Pierrepoint, the last hangman and the one responsible for hanging Ruth Ellis in July 1955. My stepfather's mother nearly fainted when she realised who she was entertaining to tea.

From this commonplace book a remedy for drying up sores. Wash sore in brandy and water and apply elder leaves, changing twice a day.

Apply a poultice of flour, honey and water with a little yeast to stop a mortification (an old word for gangrene).

Anon, Northallerton

Using cobwebs to stop bleeding has been around since Roman times and would possibly hold together the cut skin. Vinegar, alcohol, elder leaves and cranesbill all have antiseptic properties so the Shipley cobbler was doing the right thing. The following all used externally would have been useful in healing. Golden rod promotes healing, slippery elm draws out toxins and the leaves and roots of the marsh mallow soothe and control bacterial infection. Honey also has mild antiseptic properties and has been used on burns and cuts for centuries. Moss was used in military field hospitals externally for wounds and to absorb discharges. The bicarbonate of soda paste would have formed a protective cover to exclude air from the burn and prevent infection.

The current medical thinking is that you must not apply butter, creams or lotions for superficial burns and scalds but pour cold water onto the burned area for at least ten minutes, obviously not if still in contact with an electricity source. Many of us can remember being rubbed with butter when we had a burn, bump or a knock and then having a penny tied onto the bump. This was supposed to stop bruising and reduce the swelling. I suppose as a child there was some comfort if you got to keep the penny.

LEECHES

A leech is full after sucking about 25 millilitres of blood.

Leeches are worm-like parasites that feed off animals and humans by sucking the blood and were once part of every doctor's limited arsenal of remedies. Blood sucking was thought of as a cure for most diseases and reached the height of popularity in the 19th century. Leeches treated a whole range of illnesses from headaches and mental

The Leech House at Aiskew. This small, castellated building is believed to date from the late 18th or early 19th century and to have been last used for storing leeches in the early 1900s. The building and public garden in which it stands have been voluntarily restored by the Bedale District Heritage Trust.

The view from Sutton Bank looking down on Lake Gormire at the foot of Whitestone Cliff. One of Yorkshire's rare natural lakes, people believed it was bottomless. It was from here that the Bedale chemist, on his annual holiday, collected his leeches for the next year.

illness to gout and whooping cough and were used on 'congested' areas of the body to treat acute inflammation of vital organs.

A leech bite keeps the blood flowing because of a substance in their saliva which stops the blood clotting. However abhorrent we might think them, because of these very qualities, they are still of use today in micro surgery.

Leech gathering must have been the least desirable of jobs. George Walker's *The Costumes of Yorkshire 1814* described how they were collected by bare-legged women who waded into the ditches and ponds where the leeches live. They attached themselves to the women's feet and legs and were then transferred to a small barrel of water suspended round the waist.

A booklet published by the Bedale District Heritage Trust describes how in Victorian times the Bedale chemist took his annual holiday. 'He harnessed his trap and loaded a special receptacle and went to the other side of Ripon to collect "special leeches", and on his return he notified the local doctors that the leeches were available for the treatment of patients. The leeches were put in the leech house and the beck ran through the leech house to keep the leeches alive and healthy.'

Inside the Old Chemist Shop in Knaresborough, this handsome leech jar was used to store live medicinal leeches. The flat lid is perforated to allow air to enter. (By kind permission of John Farrah, Harrogate Toffee)

Den Chisholm of Marton, a Yorkshire dialect expert, recounted the story of a misunderstanding involving a leech and the age old problem of doctors not explaining things clearly.

'Old Bessy lived on the edge of a village on the North Yorkshire Moors. Her husband complained of a sore on his stomach, but being a stubborn man would not go to see the doctor. Bessy went instead. She explained that her husband was suffering from a sore on his stomach and was told by the doctor to apply the six leeches which he gave her. Now if the doctor had said, "Stick 'em on", or "clap 'em on", Bessy would have understood what to do with them. A couple of days later the doctor on seeing Bessy asked after John. "Oh, he's all reet noo", said Bessy, "but them things capped (bewildered) him, they did hooivver."

"You managed alright, did you?" asked the doctor.

"Whya, ah caan't say that wa mannished sa weel wi't fo'st un that ah gev him," said Bessy, "he chow'd on wi't, but he cudn't catch ho'd on't neea road, so ah boil'd him the rest, an he sluthered 'em doon neycly!"

WOMEN'S BUSINESS

'The nervous ailments of female constitutions, which are often induced and aggravated by tea-drinking, in advanced old age are apt to terminate in palsy. And from concomitant torpor of the absorbent system of vessels, they also very frequently terminate in general dropsy.' By a Dr Browne from papers found in a medical practice in Otley.

O n the whole Yorkshire women do not make a fuss. Collected remedies in their commonplace books referred to illnesses that affected the family, not them. If anyone had to go to the doctor and pay, women were generally last in line. I heard an expression only a few months ago from an elderly Dales' lady who had been laid low after a major operation, 'I've been very moderate,' she declared with supreme understatement.

Before the advent of women doctors the workings of the female body and mind were often a mystery to the male doctors called upon to treat them. Genteel ladies were regarded as delicate and possessing such 'female weakness' that their mental equilibrium was likely to tip over into insanity at the drop of a hat. Women of the lower orders were seen as tougher. If they survived the constant childbearing or 'bairning job' as it was called in the Dales, and the ever present danger of puerperal fever after giving birth, then they were indeed tough.

The Family Medical Adviser was published in Leeds in 1852 by John Skelton, who thought he understood female illness. 'Hysteria is a disease to which females are often subject. In cases of sudden attack put the feet at once into warm water.' He went on to advise administering various noxious substances, loosening the stays and giving an enema.

Michael Graham from near Richmond lent me a book from his

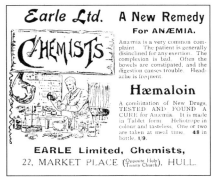

A 1906 advertisement from a souvenir of Broomfleet-with-Faxfleet Parish Sale of Work. Women were particularly prone to anaemia as the condition is made worse by pregnancy and heavy periods.

family archives, *The Family Physician* dated 1794. Written by a Maximilian Hazlemore, this doctor seemed surprisingly sympathetic to women and their problems. 'Females ought to be exceedingly cautious of what they eat or drink at the time they are "out of order". Everything that is cold, or apt to sour the stomach, ought to be avoided; fruit, butter, milk and such like.' The book goes on to advise that if a period be 'obstructed' for reasons other than pregnancy, 'proper means should be used to restore it: wholesome diet, generous liquors, cheerful

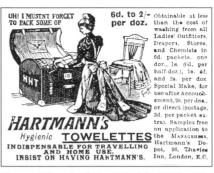

From *The Lady's World 1898. Not everyone could afford Hartmann's towelettes. Poorer women used old rags and once soiled they were boiled for use again.*

company, and all manner of amusements.' For those suffering premenstrual tension these recommendations could well cheer you up. Perhaps it might be helpful to show the list to one's partner!

Many of Michael's forebears were doctors in the north and another book dated 1841 dealt just with *The Diseases of Females.* Naturally a large section was devoted to childbirth, but here the writer favoured not interfering with nature and advising women that they were, 'at those times under the peculiar care of Providence.' No woman should rise from her bed after childbirth for at least four days and if she were unfortunate to suffer from post natal depression, an illness that Victorian doctors were familiar with, 'the strait-waistcoat must be used without delay, if the patient cannot be calmed without it.'

Slippery elm, the sterilized and washed outer bark of the red elm tree, was used if your monthly period was late. It was inserted into the vagina and kept there for about 45 minutes. It was also used for back street abortions.

Lyn Cooper, Wyke

My mother used to give me gin and hot water with some sugar for period pains.

Anon, Wensleydale

Where the wild juniper grows ... Swaledale. In this part of Yorkshire junipers were burnt on the fire to clear a house of infection, chewed to prevent fever, used in poultices for lumbago and, after boiling, in drinks for digestive problems.

Pennyroyal is a favourite herb for female derangement, removing all obstructions peculiar to women arising from obstructed perspiration.
From The Model Botanic Guide to Health by William Fox MD, published in Sheffield 1893.

In my teens in the 1920s when you were going on holiday and you were due to have a period you would take pennyroyal and hope it would come on earlier. It was a great source of amusement to mother and I that when father felt a cold coming on he wanted a brew of pennyroyal!
Edna Simpson, Bradford

In the 1800s Dr A.I. Coffin brought medical botany to Britain. Based in Leeds, his *Botanic Guide to Health* sold 40,000 copies. He advocated juniper berries 'to promote monthly terms'.

From *Every Housewife's Guide Book* price 6d, Strengthening Medicine for Delicate Girls which included carbonate of ammonia and citrate of iron to be taken in water three times daily after meals.
B. Marsh, Sheffield

WARNER'S SAFE CURE
FOR WOMEN.

Not only the best but the only remedy which can always be relied upon.

That is the verdict of every woman who has ever tried Warner's Safe Cure.

There is no better remedy for women who suffer from distressing weaknesses.

It acts like a charm in overcoming aches, pains, and bearing down sensations.

It restores the colour of health to pale cheeks, gives brightness to dull eyes, and takes away that sallow unhealthy complexion.

No woman who values her health and strength should be without the great Safe Cure.

One of the many patent medicines for women from the early 1900s. It consisted mainly of ipecacuanha, oil of aniseed and extract of mandrake – a highly poisonous plant, too much of which can induce a state of oblivion.

Granny Myatt's tonic wine especially for anaemic women: 1 quart of Tarragona (a port in northeast Spain) wine, a jar of Bovril, some extract of malt and 3 pennyworth of quinine. Scald the Bovril and malt with 1 pint of boiling water. When cold add other ingredients and mix well. A small glass every morning.

Hilda Jackson, Bedale

During pregnancy gentle physics only should be taken and tight lacing avoided. From *A Book for Every Home.*

Colin Chippindale, Great Horton

The quickest way of curing morning sickness is an outdoor privy.

Denny Minnitt, Askrigg

Raspberry leaf tea to ease childbirth.

Catharine M. Parker, Threshfield

An uncooked cabbage leaf placed in the bra when you are breastfeeding prevents soreness of nipples, or if they are sore it eases them.

Sharon Capper, Northwich*

For an abcess on the breast women used to apply a cowpat wrapped in gauze.

Jean Booth, Sheffield

I found an old book belonging to my husband's grandmother containing all sorts of undated household hints, recipes and cures. She was born in 1871 so I presume would start collecting during her early married life. For pain in the breast mix laudanum, tinctures of Benjamin, rhubarb and Hoxhams bark with 1 dram of elixir of vitriol. Take 3 teaspoons 3 times a day in a little sugar and water.

Joan Marston, Guiseley

A patronising tone from this 1950 advertisement encouraging women to smoke.

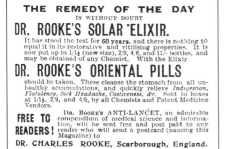

Dr Charles Rooke of Scarborough, not given to understatement. From 'The Lady's World' of 1898.

From Katy Nolan's *600 Home Recipes* – old age in women sets in at 53, in men about 60. At these particular ages, when symptoms of any kind appear, they cannot be too quickly attended to.

Mary Nolan, Stockton on Tees

Change of life. Keep bowels open, take very little alcohol, have warm baths. Husbands should exercise great patience during this irritable period. From *A Book for Every Home*.

Colin Chippindale, Great Horton

★ ★ ★ ★ ★

Any woman reading this chapter will remember the dire warnings given to us when younger. During a monthly period do not wash your hair or you will catch cold. Do not play sports as it will deplete your energy. Do not have your hair permed or it will not 'take' – there is some truth in this one. Do not eat ice cream or you will catch a chill. Do not sit on anything cold, although this last applied all the time.

★ ★ ★ ★ ★

My grandmother from Hull was a very formidable, working class woman who always wore a wrapover flowered apron unless she went to a wedding or a funeral. When I was young in the 1950s we used to sit on the kerb and if you saw her coming you jumped up pretty quick. She used to say 'You'll get kink cough in your bum'. She believed you got fever out of the drains. She was probably right.

Anne Callaghan, Hessle

Yorkshire fishermen's wives never washed their clothes on the day the men were sailing, as they thought it would wash their menfolk away.

Ann Holubecki, Redmire

Pennyroyal is a bitter astringent herb taken internally for colds, indigestion and menstrual problems so Edna Simpson's father was not so silly drinking his pennyroyal brew. Daleswomen in the past occasionally used it as an abortificant. Interestingly, it was used as a mystery ingredient in the making of black pudding in the north.

Women often suffer from the most common form of anaemia caused by lack of iron in the body. These old remedies had ingredients to combat the deficiency but there were many patent medicines available, all containing iron: Widow Welch's Female Pills, Pink Pills for Pale People and Ayer's Sarsaparilla.

Raspberry leaves have astringent and stimulating properties and have been used throughout history to encourage a safe and easy childbirth but must only be taken in the late stages of pregnancy.

Vitriol is an old name for sulphuric acid and Benjamin, otherwise known as *lindera benzoin* or spice bush, was used internally for dysentery and intestinal worms. I should think that only the laudanum helped dull the pain in the breast.

Juniper berries are used to flavour

This famous cherry brandy encouraging menopausal women of the 1930s to take to the bottle! The Change of Life to which the advertisement refers can produce some distressing symptoms but does the answer lie in the bottom of a glass?

1952 and yet another brand of iron pills. Many Yorkshire women remembered as young girls being made to take 'Pink Pills for Pale People'.

gin, a drink in which I have great faith; I have always believed it to be good for you. The berries have antiseptic and diuretic properties and stimulate the uterus. One drinks only for medicinal purposes!

The bark of *ulmus rubra* or slippery elm is now subject to legal restrictions in many countries, as for years it was used as an abortificant. However, the inner part of the bark is known to promote healing. We can imagine the desperation of women driven to seek unqualified help in unwanted pregnancies. The stigma of having a child 'out of wedlock' was very great and if the man responsible would not marry her, the woman was often consigned to a mental institution for being a degenerate in need of correction. No such punitive measures were meted out to the man.

KEEPING UP YOUR STRENGTH

'A man or woman who has to go through much toil or hardship has need of substantial nourishment but that is not to be obtained from an infusion of tea.' By Dr Browne from papers found in an Otley medical practice.

We all have those times when we feel one degree under. Tired and listless with little enthusiasm for anything much, possibly recovering from 'flu or an operation, life seems impossibly grey.

Modern day Prozac, sleeping pills, tranquillizers and all other mood enhancing medications were not available, only the rich or dissolute had access to opium. However, many patent tonic medicines contained paregoric, a form of opium, and there was always cheap alcohol. Not for nothing was gin called, 'mother's ruin'. Chlorodyne a common ingredient for cold remedies, contained a touch of chloroform and morphine and was drunk to excess by some for the latter.

So, feeling weak and run down what did people turn to for increased strength and a bit of 'pepping up'?

★ ★ ★ ★ ★

Strengthening mixture from mother's old cookery book. Put 6 whole eggs in a basin and squeeze the juice of a lemon over them and let them stand for 3 or 4 days, turning over frequently until the shell is dissolved. Then beat them together and strain through a sieve into a bottle and add half a pound of sugar, quarter of an ounce of isinglass (gelatin made from the bladders of freshwater fish), 1 pint of best rum. Shake well together. 1 tablespoon for adults and half for children.

J. Hague, Oughtibridge

I was born in Grassington and when I was growing up, if I was feeling 'under the weather', my mother would make me a drink of raw egg beaten with sugar and milk. The milk was always green top and the eggs free range and salmonella was unheard of.

Wendy Milner, Gargrave

I was born in 1913 and was not expected to live so have not done so badly, in spite of being a sickly child. The household remedy for a poor appetite was to chew dried gentian root.

Edna Simpson, Allerton

Beetroot wine if you were rundown.

Grace Handley, Settle

Cod liver oil, malt and Virol were all given to children to build you up in wartime, along with daily orange juice and school milk. The milk was heated up at nursery school with some cocoa but by the time it came round there was always skin on it. Cod liver oil was best fed to children in coffee. My father took the oil this way around 1916 and never drank coffee again until the 1960s.

Joy Calvert, Settle

From my grandmother Alice Johnson of Carleton for loss of appetite. Crushed bilberries in a glass of hot

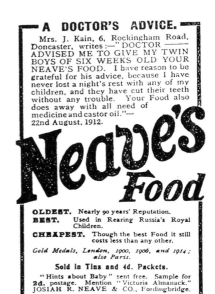

A Doncaster lady testifying to the efficacy of Neave's Food. She was in good company as it was also 'used in Rearing Russia's Royal Children.' This advertisement is dated 1914 and sadly they were all shot by the Bolsheviks in 1918.

Harrison's Restorative Camomile Pills and what splendid euphemisms: 'Weakness of the Solids' and 'Irregularities of the Female System.' From T'Bairnsla Foakes Annual Pogmoor Olmenack (sic) 1863.

milk and if no bilberries then currants will do.

For a 'pick me up' allow rose petals to dissolve into whisky or wine. After two days remove any undissolved bits then drink a glass.

If you were pining because of a thwarted love affair serve tea made from meadowsweet and biscuits made from nettles (female biscuits) and dandelion (male biscuits).

Fox Johnson, Saltaire

Strengthening mixture from my grandmother Lucy Hill.

Mix together 6 ounces each of olive oil, cod liver oil, almond oil and 6 well beaten eggs and a large tin of Nestlé's condensed milk. Take a dessertspoonful three times a day.

Ronda Ashworth, Heptonstall

My brother-in-law Raymon Lancaster was a rather delicate child. He found this remedy given to his mother in 1932 for him to take. '3 pennyworth each of Eastons Syrup, Fellows Syrup and Parrishes Food. I give my boy of nearly 14, half a teaspoon 3 times a day but your little boy will need just under a quarter of a teaspoon 3 times a day. This is a Harley Street physician's prescription and is really a very good medicine.'

D Chapman, Hornsea

I was brought up on a farm on the outskirts of Bradford. Grandma lived with us and she knew a lot of old cures. She lived to be over 100 and this was her remedy for someone who could not do a lot of exertion – it helped the heart. Pick red hawthorn berries when ripe. Put into a bottle or jam jar and cover with brandy. Leave until the liquid becomes red. Take 2 to 3 drops with a little syringe and drop onto a sugar cube. Take every day.

Lyn Cooper, Wyke

Grandfather Horace Martin, an engineering worker from Holbeck in Leeds, believed in sweet spirit of nitre. He took a spoonful in warm water if he was stopping in and a spoonful in cold water if he was going out! He believed in liquid paraffin for his bowels and he was still digging his own garden when he died at 94.

Susan Burnell, Swillington

Some interesting ingredients that would do you no harm although I am not sure about the eggshells, just think where they have been. The patent medicines for Raymon Lancaster would all have contained iron. The strengthening mixtures had a fair amount of goodness in them, not to mention the calories, but probably the alcohol was just as likely to make you feel better.

Gentian root has been known for centuries as a stimulant to the appetite and digestive system. Quinine comes from cinchona bark and has been used in homeopathy for anaemia and convalescence. Bilberries have a tonic effect and the leaves of *Rosa Gallica*, otherwise known as the apothecary's rose, were eaten for depression and lethargy. Meadowsweet is useful for many things, including soothing painful joints but unlikely to help with a broken heart!

Beetroot stimulates the immune system. Hawthorn berries have been used since the Middle Ages as a tonic for an ageing and strained heart. These little berries enlarge the coronary vessels, strengthen the heart muscles and can reduce blood pressure. No wonder old grandma lived to be over 100. Hawthorn berries were used in the past as cheap food and stewed in hard times and the leaves were called 'bread and cheese' and eaten.

Sweet spirit of nitre was formally used in Indian brandy. It settles stomach pain and dilates the blood vessels and in some circumstances causes sweating and in others acts as a diuretic. Grandfather Horace Martin therefore had most things covered.

STINKING 'SPAWS'

*'. . . for all cases of functional disorder of the liver, especially those
resulting from free living and inactive habits, combined with excess of
alcohol.' The benefits of Harrogate sulphur waters, 1875.*

An extraordinary reflection on the human condition is our
willingness to try any treatment that is uncomfortable or nasty
as it must be doing us some good. The spa towns of Harrogate and
Scarborough built a whole tourist industry on the nasty/doing good
principle.

Harrogate got there first. The Tewitt Well was discovered in 1571 by
William Slingsby of Bilton Park who saw a moneymaking opportunity
and grasped it. Other chalybeate or iron springs were discovered, in

*The Royal Pump Room Museum. In 1842 Isaac Shutt designed and built the octagonal
Pump Room for the rich and fashionable to take the water in comfortable
surroundings. The basement still houses the sulphur well and you may taste the
water for yourself – an unforgettable experience. I cannot imagine how anyone
managed two pints of the stuff.*

This sylvan scene might have been very different. Well Bank near Redmire in Wensleydale, where once a sulphurous spa well with similar properties to the Harrogate wells enjoyed something of a medical reputation with people travelling to drink its waters, until work in the neighbouring lead mines cut the flow. Now there is only a damp patch under a hawthorn bush. (Ann Holubecki)

particular 'The Stinking Spaw' in 1695; all claimed to have healing and medicinal properties.

The smell of sulphur was particularly pungent with horses refusing to go near, only humans persevered. The Harrogate waters claimed to cure rheumatism, gout, digestive ailments and skin diseases and in the 18th century drinking two pints a day was considered an effective dose.

Harrogate expanded with hotels, lodging houses, shops and entertainments. You could drink the water and bathe in it, sweating it out 'in a tub 8 feet long, the water warmed as hot as it is well bearable.' In 1842 the Pump Room was built so the rich, famous and fashionable could take their water in style. Further amenities were offered on the opening of The Royal Baths in 1897. Harrogate was a place to be seen.

Medical men would argue over which town could benefit their wealthy patients the most, with Scarborough having the added benefit of sea air. Here too the tourist industry started early, with the discovery of a spring near the South shore in 1620 by Mrs Elizabeth Farrow, who for no other reason than the water tasted horrible, decided it must be medicinal. From then on people came to drink and be purged.

The Spa and South Bay, Scarborough. The Spa was completed in 1878 and this imposing building is now a conference and entertainment centre. In front of the Spa, just off the beach, can be seen the well-head where so many came to drink the waters.

Ye Oldest Chymist Shoppe in England. This lovely building in the Market Place at Knaresborough has been in continuous use as a pharmacist's shop from 1720 to 1965 and is now owned by Farrah's Toffee Company. You can still feel the 18th-century atmosphere with the apothecary's drawers, the large pestle and mortar with gearing once turned by a dog and the red 'bleeding' couch where you sat for blood letting by the leeches from the leech jar.

Scarborough styled itself the 'Queen of the Watering Places' and could offer added attractions like sea bathing. As early as 1735 you could take to the water in one of the new-fangled bathing machines, being careful to alight on the seaward side away from the prurient gaze of male loiterers.

For a time Knaresborough gave both Harrogate and Scarborough a run for their money. It claimed to have superior accommodation and possibly the oldest tourist attraction in the country; Mother Shipton's Cave and Petrifying Well. The petrifying waters of the Dropping Well were said to relieve any 'flux' and must at least have tasted better than the stuff being served up in Harrogate.

Knaresborough also offered the services of the apothecary John Beckwith who dealt in herbal remedies and quills filled with quicksilver, believed to be helpful in the fight against illness ... and witches.

Whatever the various merits of these Yorkshire towns, of one thing we can be certain; there was money to be made in catering for the truly sick or the hypochondriac.

10 TOP TIPS FROM YORKSHIRE

- A tablespoon of limewater taken in a little milk in a morning keeps a person in good health.

- Cold meats are generally found more easy of digestion than warm ones.

- To have rosy children give them plenty of apples and scalded milk.

- Cast not a clout till May be out.

- Exercise should never be continued to weariness.

- Stout persons with short necks and florid countenances, should avoid too much animal food, wine, spirits and especially malt liquors, excitement and hot rooms.

- Inflammation of the body is often caused by an over-hot bath.

- On selecting a good adviser and reliable friend look for the Roman nose and large hand.

- Rise early and never sit up late.

- Keep the feet warm, the head cool and the bowels open.